ELECTROMAGNETISM
and its Applications

ELECTROMAGNETISM
and its Applications

an introduction

B. Bolton

School of Electrical Engineering
University of Bath

VNR **UK** Van Nostrand Reinhold (UK) Co. Ltd.

© 1980, B. Bolton

Reprinted 1981, 1982, 1984, 1986, 1987, 1988

Published by Van Nostrand Reinhold (UK) Co. Ltd.
Molly Millars Lane, Wokingham, Berkshire, England

Library of Congress Cataloging in Publication Data
Bolton, B
  Electromagnetism and its applications.

  Includes index.
  1. Electric engineering.   2. Electromagnetism.
3. Electrostatics.   I. Title.
TK153.B59   621.3   79-13903
ISBN 0-442-30243-6
ISBN 0-442-30244-4 pbk.

Printed and bound in Hong Kong

CONTENTS

CHAPTER 1

Introduction

This book is written for students who need to understand the principles of electromagnetism. It is intended to be an aid to learning and as such it is addressed directly to the student.

The book is based on material that has been used successfully by several hundred students of electrical engineering at the University of Bath. They have shown enthusiasm for the approach used here and it is hoped that you too will find the text interesting and helpful. If the book is used properly it should help you to master the principles of the subject. Those of you who wish to take the subject further should then be able to move on with confidence to the more advanced and traditional textbooks.

The mathematical parts of the subject have been gathered together in a series of Tasks. These cover the essential principles of the theory as an engineering student might need to know them. Each Task begins with a statement of what you are expected to achieve and ends with a series of problems which you can use to test your achievement. The problems will also help you to understand the material better and you should look upon them as an essential part of the learning process. The Tasks are self-contained and you should be able to complete each one in a relatively short time. You should try to work through the book Task by Task. This way you will be able to mark up a series of successes as each Task is completed to your satisfaction. Your learning will then be much more effective.

The non-mathematical ideas and concepts are not presented as 'theory'. Instead, they are introduced naturally in the chapters on applications which are sandwiched amongst the Tasks. These applications have been chosen for their interest, novelty and breadth of appeal. It is important that you read these chapters so that you can gain a full appreciation of the subject. I hope that in so doing, you will realise that this is an applied subject and as such is of interest to anyone concerned with electrical engineering. This is a fact that is often obscured in the more theoretical studies of electromagnetism. The theory is of course essential, but what we should realise is that the theory is based on experimental observation. We begin by developing a theory to explain what we observe and then we extend the theory to predict events that we might not otherwise have seen. We should never allow ourselves to be so carried away by the theory that we end up proving the very facts on which the theory is based. We do not 'prove' that electrostatic forces exist, we observe it as a fact—as the ancient Greeks did. We do not 'prove' that magnetic materials are influenced by a magnetic field, we observe it—as the ancient Chinese did with the first magnetic compass, and we do not 'prove' that there is a force between two current-carrying conductors—we observe it.

I hope that you will find this book interesting and useful, and I wish you success and pleasure in your studies.

Should you wish to proceed to more advanced texts you would do well to consider G. W. Carter's book, *The Electromagnetic Field in its Engineering Aspects*, published by Longman, or alternatively P. Hammond's book, *Applied Electromagnetism*, published by Pergamon Press.

CHAPTER 2

Static electricity or When to keep your shirt on

2.1 INTRODUCTION

Electrostatics is a fascinating subject. Electrostatic phenomena of various kinds have held the imagination of people for thousands and thousands of years. Undoubtedly the most dramatic manifestation of electrostatic forces occurs in the thunderstorm and this has been a source of wonder and fear in all civilisations. The cause has been variously attributed to gods, giants and demons, and our ancestors would be incredulous of a modern explanation. By the same token, mariners of old would find a modern explanation of St Elmo's fire totally unacceptable. The fire of St Elmo is no more than a corona discharge which lights up the rigging of sailing ships under certain unusual atmospheric conditions, but in a non-scientific age it was given religious significance.

Today, most of the magic of electrostatics has gone, but the fascination remains. Our understanding of the subject enables us to build huge electrostatic machines which help to keep our atmosphere clean. We can make electrostatic machines that can copy, machines that can paint, machines that can separate powders or make artificial velvet, and high-voltage machines that the physicist can use in his exploration of matter.

There is a story told of a nomadic tribe which religiously carried about with it a large electrostatic device. When touching this device the elders of the tribe wore elaborate garments of woven gold to shield themselves from the effects of the electrostatic field. It was forbidden for any other member of the tribe to touch the precious object. The following passage describes what happened to one unfortunate individual who, with the best of intentions, broke this law.

And when they came to Nachan's threshing floor,
Uzzah put forth his hand to the ark of God, and
took hold of it : for the oxen shook it.
And the anger of the Lord was kindled against
Uzzah ; and God smote him there for his
error ; and there he died by the ark of God.

2 Samuel 6 :6

It would appear that Uzzah died from an electrical discharge that came from the ark of the covenant. The ark was in fact a wooden chest, lined inside and out with gold. It was raised on wooden legs which were also covered with gold and the whole arrangement made a very effective electrical capacitor. In the dry, dusty winds of the desert this capacitor would have become charged to a high potential.

The robes of these ancient priests have a modern counterpart. The Central Electricity Generating Board has developed metalised suits to be worn by men working on extra-high-voltage transmission lines. With these suits on, the men can work safely even with the voltage supply still on the lines. So how do these suits work? To understand this we need to understand what it is we mean by 'charge' and we need to know a little about how a body becomes charged.

2.2 CHARGED BODIES

Nobody really knows what 'charge' is. What we do know is that matter has two properties that give rise to forces. One is the property of mass, which gives rise to gravitational forces and the other is the property of charge which gives rise to electric forces. Gravitational forces are always attractive. Electric forces may be attractive or repulsive. The physicists tell us that matter is made up of a number of small particles. The most common ones are the neutron, the proton and the electron. Moreover, we are told that electric forces occur between the electron and the proton, between the electron and other electrons, and between two protons. The force between the electron and the proton tends to pull the particles together whereas the forces between two electrons and between two protons tend to force these particles apart. The other interesting fact is that a body with equal numbers of protons and electrons in it is electrically neutral, i.e. it will not produce an electric force on nearby electrons. We can deduce from this that the charges on electrons and protons are self-cancelling. If we say that the charge on these particles is of opposite sign, so that the two together sum to zero, this fact can be allowed for. For historical reasons, which need not concern us, the charge on the electron is assumed to be negative and the charge on the proton is assumed positive.

What then is a 'charged' body? The simple answer is that it is a body that has more electrons than protons, or more protons than electrons. In the first case we would

2

say that it was negatively charged. In the second case it would be positively charged.

Suppose that we had a large metal sphere raised on insulating supports so that any charge on it would not leak away to earth. Then suppose we blew over it a stream of positively charged dust particles. The metal, being a conductor of electricity, would by its very nature have within it many, many free electrons. By this we mean electrons that are not locked on to the atomic lattice of the material. The first particle to land on the sphere would collect some of this electronic charge and the charge would be held tightly to the particle by the very large electric force of attraction between the electron and the protons on the particle. As the particle was blown or knocked away it would take with it some of the electronic charge of the sphere. The sphere, we assume, was originally in a neutral condition. After this contact it has less electronic charge than it started with so that it must now be positively charged. This process will continue with the sphere becoming more and more positively charged until it is so positive that it repels all incoming dust particles.

Now let us consider what is happening inside the sphere. We know that it now has too much positive charge. We also know that positive charges repel each other. So, the positive charge in the sphere will try to spread itself out. If it were free to move through space it would drift off in all directions, rather like a packet of peas exploding in slow motion. However, it cannot move through space and the 'explosion' has to stop when the charge reaches the surface of the metal. The final picture has the excess charge spread out evenly over the surface of the sphere. Many years ago Michael Faraday had himself shut up in a metal box together with field measuring instruments. The box was charged and Faraday showed conclusively that there was no electric effect within the box. The charge that had spread over the outside of the conducting box had no net result inside. As far as Faraday was concerned the box might just as well have been at earth potential. This then is the secret of the Priest's golden robes and of the metal suits of the men who work close to high voltage lines. The conducting suits act in the same way as Faraday's box. The people inside are not affected by the charge on the outside.

Incidentally, don't try it. High voltages have to be treated with great caution.

2.3 CHARGING PROCESSES

We have not yet said how the dust particles become charged. There are several possibilities. The air itself is continuously being ionised by cosmic rays and radio-activity. And what do we mean by ionisation? Briefly

this. A particle can absorb energy from radiations. This energy input may be sufficient to cause the ejection from the particle of an electron. We then have an electron which is negatively charged and the remainder which will be positively charged. If the electron is collected by another neutral particle then that particle will become negatively charged. This is a continuous process and it is balanced by a continuous process of recombination as the electrons are collected by positively charged particles.

We have then ionisation as one possible cause of particle charging. Another is due to water action. As water splashes and as small bubbles in water burst, tiny drops of charged water are thrown into the air. These can be carried away by the wind and as the water evaporates the charge is left behind on whatever remains. Then there is contact electrification. This is what takes place when insulating rods are rubbed with cloths to produce charge. What happens is in fact very complex, but a straightforward explanation would be as follows.

When two materials come into contact there is the possibility of charge transfer between them. If the materials are conductors there is usually a transfer of electrons from one surface to the other. The electrons on one surface find the electrical conditions in the other surface more attractive and move over. If one of the materials is an insulator the conditions at the interface of the two materials may be affected by the presence on the insulator surface of charged particles. In this case the transfer may be a transfer of positively charged particles and not electrons. Whatever the mechanism, the fact is that dissimilar surfaces will have slightly different electrical conditions in them. When two such surfaces are brought together the difference is neutralised by charge transfer. If the surfaces are then moved apart, one goes away with more negative charge than it had to begin with and the other with more positive charge. As the process is repeated, the charge difference builds up and very large voltages can be produced. Such voltages can cause sparks and sparks can cause explosions.

In recent years five super-tankers have exploded as a result of sparks caused by electrostatic charge generation. In 1964 it was estimated that about 1000 Americans a year died as a result of explosions in hospital operating theatres. And there is on record the unfortunate case of a person who answered the call of nature in a primitive lavatory. The removal of clothing, made from synthetic materials, caused a spark which ignited a pocket of methane gas. So do be careful where you remove your shirt.

FURTHER READING

Electrostatics and its Applications, A. D. Moore, J. Wiley & Sons, 1973.

CHAPTER 3

Task 1: Charges and forces

T1.1 INTRODUCTION

If we are to make precise predictions about electro-static events then we need a precise model of electro-statics. We cannot hope to build a physical model so we have to resort to a mathematical one. The mathematics we will use in this book is not very advanced. You have probably met it all before. In this Task, for example, you will need to resolve forces and do some straight-forward arithmetic—no more.

The purpose of this Task is to introduce to you the inverse–square law as applied to very small charged spheres in space. We then define an important constant. Finally, by reason and discussion, we extend our ideas from spherical to planar and cylindrical geometries. This is very important because it takes us from the imaginary world of point charges in space towards the real world of capacitors, cables and transmission circuits.

T1.2 OBJECTIVES

When you have finished this Task you should be able to do the following:

(a) explain in your own words what the inverse–square law of electrostatics means;
(b) define the primary electric constant in terms of the constant of proportionality in the inverse–square law;
(c) determine the force acting between two small, charged spheres a known distance apart in air;
(d) determine the resultant force acting on a small, charged sphere a known distance away from several other small, charged spheres;
(e) deduce that the force on a charged particle above a large, flat, charged sheet acts along a line perpendicular to the sheet; and
(f) deduce that the force on a charged particle near a long, charged cylinder acts along the line of the radius from the axis of the cylinder passing through the particle.

4

T1.3 THE INVERSE–SQUARE LAW

It is possible to produce an excess of positive or negative charge on a conducting or an insulating body. For the present we shall consider conducting bodies only. Let us imagine that we had two small, conducting spheres with a charge Q_1 on one sphere and Q_2 on the other. We could demonstrate fairly easily that there was a force between the spheres due to the two charges. Some careful experimentation would show that this force varied in direct proportion to the magnitudes of the charge Q_1 and the charge Q_2, and in inverse proportion to the square of the distance between the centres of the spheres. We would record this conclusion as follows:

$$F \propto \frac{Q_1 Q_2}{r^2} \tag{T1.1}$$

where F is the force and r the distance between centres.

Now force is a vector quantity and we must define its direction. For positive values of Q_1 and Q_2 the force will tend to move the spheres apart. The line of action of the force will be the line joining the two centres.

Question 1

Two small conducting spheres carry positive charges Q_1 and Q_2. They are separated by a distance of 1 m, measured between centres, and experience a force of repulsion of 36 newtons. If the two spheres are now moved so that the distance between centres becomes 3 m, what will be the new value of the repulsive force?

T1.4 A NOTE ON UNITS

The system of units adopted as standard in electrical engineering is the SI system. The fundamental units are the metre, kilogram, second and ampere. From these four all other units are derived. The derived unit of force is the newton (N) and the derived unit of charge is the coulomb (C).

To complete equation T1.1 we need a constant of proportionality. Once the four fundamental units have been selected this constant is fixed for us. In the SI system it has a value very nearly equal to $9\ 10^9$. Thus for charged spheres in a vacuum, equation T1.1 would become:

$$F = 9\ 10^9 \cdot \frac{Q_1 Q_2}{r^2}\ \text{newtons} \qquad (T1.2)$$

We prefer to write this equation in the following way:

$$F = \frac{1}{4\pi\varepsilon_0} \cdot \frac{Q_1 Q_2}{r^2}\ \text{newtons} \qquad (T1.3)$$

It follows that ε_0 has the value $10^{-9}/36\pi$. The units are farads per metre (F m^{-1}). The constant ε_0 is known as the permittivity of free space. The 4π term in the denominator has been isolated because we can identify the term $4\pi r^2$ as the surface area of a sphere of radius r and this is useful to us later.

Question 2

Two small conducting spheres are separated by a distance 3 m between centres and carry charges 10^{-9}C and 10^{-7}C respectively. Calculate the magnitude of the force of repulsion between spheres due to the presence of the charge on the spheres.

Note that the important distance is the distance between centres. Although we showed in the previous chapter that the charge on a charged sphere collected on the outside surface of the sphere, outside bodies are affected as if the whole charge were concentrated at the centre.

T1.5 SUPERPOSITION OF FORCES

So far we have considered only two charged spheres. How do we deal with the problem of many such spheres? Figure T1.1 illustrates the case of four charged spheres at the corners of a plane square of 1 m side. The charge on each sphere is 10^{-6}C. What is the resultant force acting on the sphere at point C?

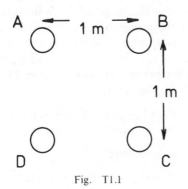

Fig. T1.1

There are in fact three component forces: one due to the charge at A acting along the line of action AC; one due to the charge at B, acting along the line of action BC, and one due to the charge at D, acting along the line DC.

Force on C due to A,

$$F_A = \frac{Q_A Q_C}{4\pi\varepsilon_0 (AC)^2} = \frac{9\ 10^9\ 10^{-6}\ 10^{-6}}{(\sqrt{2})^2} = 4.5\ 10^3\ \text{N}$$

Force on C due to B,

$$F_B = \frac{Q_B Q_C}{4\pi\varepsilon_0 (BC)^2} = \frac{9.10^9\ 10^{-6}\ 10^{-6}}{1} = 9\ 10^{-3}\ \text{N}$$

Force on C due to D,

$$F_D = \frac{Q_D Q_C}{4\pi\varepsilon_0 (DC)^2} = \frac{9\ 10^9\ 10^{-6}\ 10^{-6}}{1} = 9\ 10^{-3}\ \text{N}$$

The diagram of forces is shown in figure T1.2. The resultant force is clearly in the direction of F_A and will have a magnitude equal to:

$$F = 4.5\ 10^{-3} + \sqrt{(9\ 10^{-3})^2 + (9\ 10^{-3})^2}$$

$$= 17.2\ 10^{-3}\ \text{N}$$

Now try the self-assessment questions.

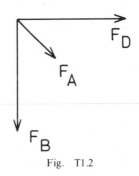

Fig. T1.2

T1.6 SELF-ASSESSMENT QUESTIONS

Question 3

Determine the magnitude and direction of the resultant forces on Q_1, Q_2 and Q_3 in figure T1.3 for the following conditions:

(a) $Q_1 = Q_2 = Q_3 = 10^{-6}$ C
(b) $Q_1 = Q_3 = 10^{-6}$ C; $Q_2 = -10^{-6}$ C

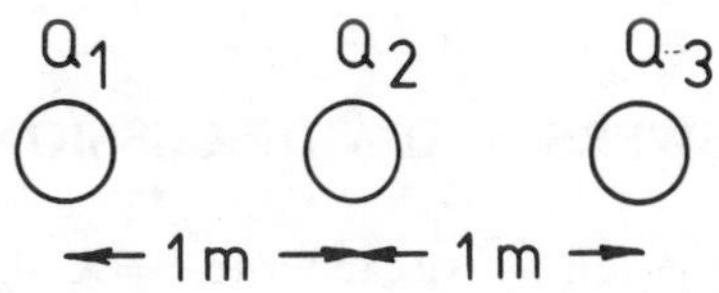

Fig. T1.3

Question 4

Three small charged spheres lie at the corners of an equilateral triangle with sides of length 2 m. The magnitude of each charge is $4 \cdot 10^{-6}$ C. Calculate the magnitude and direction of the resultant forces on each charge.

Question 5

Eight small charged spheres are placed at the corners of a cube of 1 m side as in figure T1.4. Spheres at A, B, C and D each carry charges of -10^{-6} C. Spheres at E, F, G and H each carry charges of $+10^{-6}$ C. Determine the resultant force acting on a charge of 1 coulomb situated at the centre of the cube (i.e. equidistant from all corners).

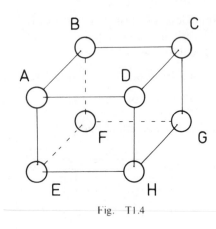

Fig. T1.4

Question 6

Four equal charges are placed on a line in the positions shown in figure T1.5. Determine the magnitude and direction of the resultant force acting on the charge q, in terms of Q and q.

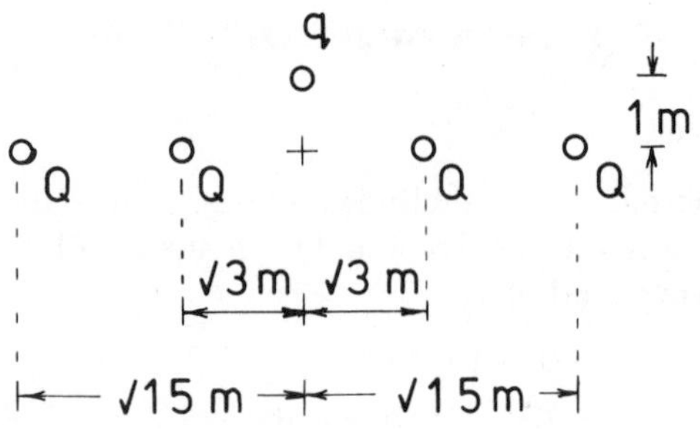

$$q$$

$$Q \qquad Q \qquad + \qquad Q \qquad Q$$

$$\sqrt{3}\,m \quad \sqrt{3}\,m$$

$$\sqrt{15}\,m \quad \sqrt{15}\,m$$

1 m

Fig. T1.5

T1.7 ANSWERS AND A DISCUSSION

1. From equation 1.1 we can write $F = K \cdot 1/r^2$, where K is constant. Hence $K = 36.(1)^2 = 36$ N m^2

$$\therefore F_2 = K/r_2^2 = 36/9 = 4 \text{ N}$$

2. $F = 9 \cdot 10^9 \cdot 10^{-9} \cdot 10^{-7}/9 = 10^{-7}$ N
3. (a) Force on $Q_1 = 9 \cdot 10^9 \cdot 10^{-12} + 9 \cdot 10^9 \cdot 10^{-12}/4$
   $= 11.25 \cdot 10^{-3}$ N acting along the line of centres away from Q_2;
   Force on Q_2 is zero;
   Force on Q_3 is $11.25 \cdot 10^{-3}$ N acting along the line of centres away from Q_2.
   (b) Force on Q_1 is $6.75 \cdot 10^{-3}$ N acting along the line of centres towards Q_2;
   Force on Q_2 is zero;
   Force on Q_3 is $6.75 \cdot 10^{-3}$ N acting along the line of centres towards Q_2.
4. Force on C due to charge at $A = F_A$

$$= \frac{9 \cdot 10^9 \cdot 16 \cdot 10^{-12}}{4} = 36 \cdot 10^{-3} \text{ N}$$

Force on C due to charge at $B = F_B$

$$= 36 \cdot 10^{-3} \text{ N}$$

Resultant $= F_A \cos 30 + F_B \cos 30 = 62.4 \cdot 10^{-3}$ N acting in the sense shown in figure T1.6.

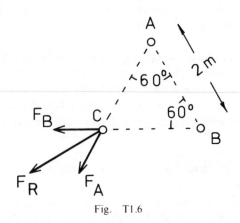

Fig. T1.6

By symmetry, the resultant forces on charges at A and B will have the same magnitudes and the directions will be along the perpendicular bisectors through A and B.

5. Let us look first at the effect of the charges at E and G. The one-coulomb charge will be at the intersection of the lines joining opposite corners of the cube. It will be forced away from E along the line EC and away from G along the line GA. We could represent these forces on the plane $EACG$ as in figure T1.7.

Resolving horizontally:

Resultant, $F_H = F_G \cos \theta - F_E \cos \theta$, but F_G equals F_E in magnitude, $\therefore F_H = 0$

Resolving vertically:

Resultant, $F_V = (F_G + F_E) \sin \theta = 1.4 \cdot 10^4$ N

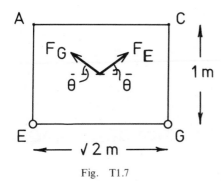

Fig. T1.7

The effect of charges at F and H will be exactly the same, so the resultant vertical force due to the positive charges will be 2.8×10^4 N.

The effect of the four negative charges on top of the cube can be seen to be exactly the same as the effect of the four positive charges on the bottom. Therefore the total upwards force on the one-coulomb charge will be 5.6×10^4 N.

Two points of interest emerge. Firstly, the force is considerable. This is because we have introduced a charge of one coulomb (or unit charge, as it is known). This is a very large quantity of charge and well outside normal practical experience. However, we often introduce the idea of unit charge into problem situations as part of a 'What would happen if . . . ?' exercise. We shall certainly meet it again. The second interesting point is that this solution gives us a clue as to what happens to charges that find themselves above large, flat, charged plates. We decided above that the effect of charges E and G was to push the unit charge vertically upwards. If the unit charge were above an infinite charged plane then for every charge E, there

would be a corresponding charge G. The resultant force due to each pair would be vertically upwards. No horizontal component of force would result. Therefore we can conclude that any charge above a large charged sheet would be forced in a direction perpendicular to the plane of the sheet.

6. The four forces acting on q are represented in figure T1.8. It should be clear that F_1 will equal F_4 in magnitude and F_2 will equal F_3. It should also be clear that the components of the forces in the direction parallel to the line will sum to zero. The resultant vertical force will be the sum of the vertically resolved components of F_1, F_2, F_3 and F_4 and your answer should be $F = 2.5 \, Qq \, 10^9$ N.

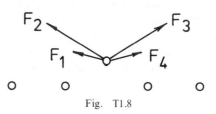

Fig. T1.8

Now suppose that we had an infinitely long line with equal, positive charges uniformly spread along it. A charge q placed R metres from it would be pushed away. From what we have said above, there would be no component of force parallel to the line. The resultant acts radially outwards from the line through q. But notice that all the points distance R from the line define a cylinder of radius R. Any positive charge placed on this surface would be forced radially away from the surface. Remember this because we will want to make use of the fact later.

CHAPTER 4

Electrostatic copiers and chimneys that don't smoke

4.1 INTRODUCTION

Electrical engineering is the art of harnessing electric forces and using them to our advantage. In Task 1 we considered electrostatic forces acting on small charged spheres. In this chapter we shall look at two applications in which these forces are put to use for our benefit. The first case we consider is the electrostatic copier. The second is the electrostatic precipitator. Both have important roles to play, the first in commerce, the second in industry.

4.2 XEROGRAPHY

Xerography is the word used to describe the electrostatic copying of documents. The basic process is as follows. Positive charge is sprayed onto a drum which has a layer of photoconductive material on its outer curved surface. So long as the drum is kept in the dark the charge remains spread over the surface. However, if light falls on the photoconductive layer then electrons are released in that layer. These electrons combine with the local positive charge on the surface and neutralise it. When a document is to be copied an image of the document is projected onto the dark drum. Positive charge is neutralised under the light pattern by electrons which are released in the photoconductor. This leaves behind a pattern of positive charge which is identical to the original black pattern on the document.

The next step in the copying process is to pour a negatively charged marker material on to the drum. This sticks to the drum wherever there is positive charge. This gives us a pattern of marker material which is identical to the original black pattern on the document. The drum is then rolled over a sheet of white paper and the pattern of marker material is transferred to the paper.

The final stage in the process is the fixing of the marker material, often called the toner, into a permanent inked image. The various stages in the process are described in a little more detail below.

4.3 CHARGING THE SURFACE OF THE DRUM

We already know that a positively charged cylinder will drive positive charge away from it and attract negative charge to it. Suppose we position a conducting cylinder above a conducting sheet and charge them respectively positive and negative by connecting a voltage supply (d.c.) between them with the positive terminal going to the cylinder. What would happen to any free charge that appeared in the space between the conductors?

If the free charge were positive it would be driven to the negatively charged surface. There it would neutralise part of the negative charge on the plate. The loss in electronic charge would be made up by electron flow from the voltage source. Now suppose that we lay an insulating layer on top of the conducting sheet. How would this modify the process?

The effect of the insulating layer is represented in figure 4.1. The positive charge cannot pass through the insulating layer. It must therefore lie on it. This is the process we use to lay down a layer of positive charge on an insulating sheet. If we bend the sheet around to form a drum then we can lay charge on the outer curved surface by rotating the drum under the charged cylinder. We shall not concern ourselves here with how we produce the free charges. We can consider that in a later chapter.

4.4 THE PHOTOCONDUCTOR

The most commonly used material for this is amorphous selenium. In the dark this will behave as an insulator and there will be no charge transfer through it. When a photon of light strikes the surface it transfers energy to the material which causes the atomic lattice to release electronic charge. If the surface layer has been charged positively then the electrons that are produced by the light will be attracted to the surface. There they will neutralise part of the positive charge. Positive charge remains where no light falls. In many machines the photoconductive layer is laid on top of a very thin insulating layer of alumina on an aluminium drum.

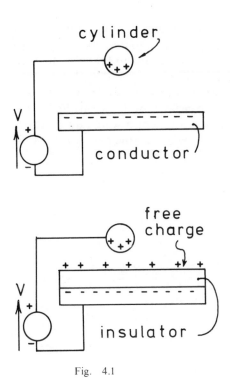

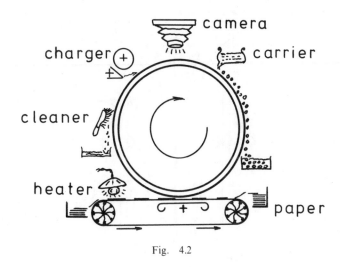

Fig. 4.2

Fig. 4.1

4.5 DEVELOPMENT

The next problem we need to consider is how to get the pattern of positive charge printed onto a piece of paper. We have already suggested a solution—to pour a negatively charged marker material over the pattern of positive charge. But how do we charge the marker material? The answer is, by contact electrification.

The marker material is carried on the surface of tiny plastic beads. These beads have typical diameters of 10×10^{-6} m (or 10 microns). The beads are mixed up with larger glass beads, called carriers, of about 750×10^{-6} m diameter. The mixture is agitated and the two sets of particles become charged by contact electrification, rather like dust particles in a wind. The marker particles become negative and the carriers positive. This combination is now poured over the charge pattern on the drum. Some of the negative toner is picked up by the positive charge on the drum. The rest is held by the carriers and taken off the drum to a collecting tray. The carriers therefore help to keep the marker off those parts of the drum surface where no positive charge pattern exists.

The drum now rolls over a sheet of paper and the marker material is printed on to the paper. This transfer is helped by yet another electrostatic process. Behind the paper is a positively charged metal plate. This acts to pull the negatively charged marker off the drum and on to the paper. Once the paper is marked, it is fed

through a heater where the marker material is fused into a permanent dry image.

4.6 ELECTROSTATIC PRECIPITATION

The electrostatic precipitator is a device for removing dust and grit from gases. This it does very well. A properly designed precipitator can remove more than 99 per cent of all the dust and grit from a gas. Just how important this process is to society can be judged from the following figures. It was estimated in 1973 that 20 million tons of dust was precipitated annually from the flue gases of power stations in the United States. The dust in question has the appearance of fine face-powder and wet or dry is most unpleasant.

In its simplest form the precipitator consists of a long metal tube with a fine metal wire down its axis. The dirty gas is blown in at one end and clean gas emerges at the other. The tube is connected to the positive side of a high-voltage source of direct current. The thin wire is connected to the negative side. The movement of charge in the conductors is then such as to cause an excess of positive charge on the tube and an excess of negative charge on the wire. If the voltage is high enough, say 50 000 V for a 30 cm diameter tube, the fine wire causes a corona discharge in the gas. Now this is something we have not yet met and will look at in more detail later. It is sufficient to say here that the electrical conditions around the wire are such that gas in the vicinity of the wire is ionised. Electronic charge is thus released in the gas. This charge attaches itself to dust particles in the gas and the charged particle is then subject to the effects of the electric forces. The process is illustrated in figure 4.3. The negatively charged particles are attracted by the positive charge on the tube and repelled by the negative charge on the wire. There

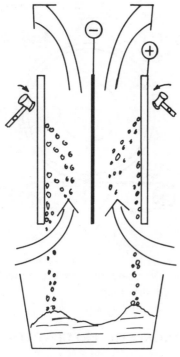

Fig. 4.3

is thus an accumulation of negatively charged dust on the tube. Every so often the tube is given a sharp knock and this causes the dust to fall away from the wall and drop into a collector below the tube.

Precipitators range in size from the small domestic varieties for installation in private homes to the largest industrial versions which would dwarf a row of houses. All use the same basic principle of electrostatic attraction and repulsion.

CHAPTER 5

Task 2: Electric field strength and potential energy

T2.1 INTRODUCTION

The electric field strength at a point is simply defined as the electrostatic force that would be exerted on a charge of 1 coulomb if it were placed at that point. If the force were due to a known array of point charges then we could calculate it using methods similar to those used in section T1.5. The concept of electric field strength is very useful. The strength of electrical insulation, for example, is always given in terms of electric field strength and the strength of a radio signal at a point in space is also measured in terms of electric field strength.

The idea of potential energy in the electric field is important because it enables us to understand what we mean by a 'volt' and a knowledge of energy storage will help us to understand the principles of electro-mechanical actuators such as electrostatic microphones and loud-speakers.

T2.2 OBJECTIVES

When you have completed the unit you should be able to do the following:

(a) define electric field strength as the force that would act on a unit charge;
(b) calculate the electric field strength at points about groups of point charges;
(c) calculate the potential energy of a group of point charges;
(d) calculate the change in potential energy as a charge is moved from one point to another in the presence of other charges; and
(e) answer the self-assessment questions correctly.

T2.3 ELECTRIC FIELD STRENGTH

Question 1

Referring to figure T2.1, what is the magnitude of the force on the point charge Q_1 due to the presence of the point charge Q_2?

Question 2

Is this force a vector or scalar quantity?

The force on Q_1 due to the presence of Q_2 is given by:

$$F = \frac{Q_1 Q_2}{4\pi\varepsilon_0 r^2} = Q_1 \frac{Q_2}{4\pi\varepsilon_0 r^2} \qquad \text{(T2.1)}$$

writing

$$\frac{Q_2}{4\pi\varepsilon_0 r^2} = E_2$$

we have

$$F = Q_1 E_2 \qquad \text{(T2.2)}$$

E_2 is defined as the electric field strength due to Q_2 at the point in space occupied by Q_1. It may be thought of as a measure of the influence of Q_2 at point Q_1.

Why do we need to develop this idea of electric field strength? If you could suspend a charged particle at a point in space, say about 50 cm in front of your nose, you would find that the particle would experience electrostatic forces. These would be as a result of charges existing in the environment around the particle. You yourself are probably charged, particularly if you are wearing clothes made from synthetic materials. Metal objects in the room may be charged, particularly if they are standing on a nylon carpet in a position where people can brush against them, and of course there is charge in the atmosphere. It would be impossible to calculate the individual contribution of each of these sources of charge to the total force on the particle, but if we could somehow arrive at a figure for the electric field strength at the point we could then substitute directly into equation T2.2 and predict what the force would be. As we develop our ideas of electrostatics we shall find it easier to talk in terms of electric field strength than in terms of the effects of particular charges.

If Q_1 in equation T2.2 were a charge of 1 coulomb, then the force F would be numerically equal to the electric field strength E. Thus we can define the electric field strength at a point in space as the force that would be exerted on a charge of 1 coulomb placed at that point.

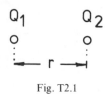

Fig. T2.1

Question 3

Is E a vector or a scalar quantity?

Question 4

Referring to figure T2.1; what is the electric field strength at the point in space occupied by Q_2 due to the presence of the charge Q_1?

If you are not sure of the answer to this then go back to the beginning of this section and see what happens if you interchange the terms Q_1 and Q_2 throughout.

The following questions refer to the arrangement of point charges shown in figure T2.2

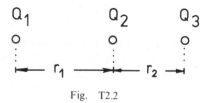

Fig. T2.2

Question 5

What is the magnitude of the force on Q_2 due to the charge Q_3 and what is its direction?

Question 6

What is the magnitude of the force on Q_2 due to the charge Q_1 and what is its direction?

Question 7

What is the magnitude of the electric field strength at the point Q_2 due to Q_3 and what is its direction?

Question 8

What is the magnitude of the electric field strength at the point Q_2 due to Q_1 and what is its direction?

Question 9

What is the magnitude of the resultant force on Q_2 due to Q_1 and Q_3 and what is its direction?

Question 10

What is the resultant electric field strength at the point Q_2 due to Q_1 and Q_3 and what is its direction?

Now compare the answers to Questions 9 and 10 and note that one is Q_2 times the other. In other words, the *resultant* force on Q_2 is equal to the *resultant* electric field strength at Q_2 multiplied by Q_2. (cf. equation 2.2). The units of E are volts/metre (V m^{-1}).

T2.4 POTENTIAL ENERGY

If we have two point charges Q_1 and Q_2 the force between them is given by the inverse–square law. If we attempt to move Q_2 closer to Q_1 we must do work against this force. In an electrostatic system it is generally true that there is no loss of energy, i.e. an electrostatic system of forces is a conservative system. This being so, the work done against a force must appear as an increase in the potential energy of the system.

Let us take a charge Q_1 and put it down somewhere in space, remote from all other charge. No work has to be expended in doing this. But, if we now bring up another charge Q_2 and place it a distance a from Q_1 we have to do work overcoming the repulsive force between Q_1 and Q_2. How much potential energy does the system then possess? The easiest way to find out is to release one charge and let it move away from the other charge, then work out how much energy is expended in this movement. This energy must be equal to the potential energy released.

We start off then with the arrangement shown in the left-hand side of figure T2.3 with Q_1 and Q_2 separated by

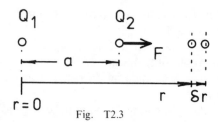

Fig. T2.3

a distance a. The force F causes Q_2 to move away from Q_1. Let it move to some general distance r from Q_1. The force on Q_2 at this distance r is given by:

$$F_r = E_r Q_2 = \frac{Q_1 Q_2}{4\pi\varepsilon_0 r^2} \qquad \text{(T2.3)}$$

Let the charge Q_2 move a further, and small, distance δr. What is the small amount of work done by the system during this movement?

$$\delta \text{WD} = F_r \cdot \delta r \qquad \text{(T2.4)}$$

The total work done by the system as the two charges separate completely will be the sum of all the small amounts δWD across all the small distances δr. Thus:

$$\text{Total work done} = \sum F_r \delta r \qquad \text{(T2.5)}$$

Now where do we begin our summation, and where do we end? We begin at the start of the movement when r has a particular value $r = a$; we end at the point where the two charges no longer influence each other—in short where $F_r = 0$. This occurs as $r \to \infty$.

Putting these limits in equation T2.5 gives:

$$\text{Total work done} = \sum_{r=a}^{r=\infty} F_r \delta r \qquad \text{(T2.6)}$$

and in the limit, as $\delta r \to 0$ this becomes:

$$\text{Total work done} = \int_{r=a}^{r=\infty} F_r \, dr = \int_{r=a}^{r=\infty} \frac{Q_1 Q_2}{4\pi\varepsilon_0 r^2} \, dr \quad \text{(T2.7)}$$

$$= \frac{Q_1 Q_2}{4\pi\varepsilon_0} \frac{1}{a} \qquad \text{(T2.8)}$$

Thus, the potential energy of Q_2 when a distance a from Q_1 is given by equation T2.8.

In solutions of this kind, a proportion of students regularly forget that the force varies as the distance varies. Try not to make that mistake.

Now for a short question.

Question 11

A point charge Q_2 is half a metre away from a point charge Q_1. How close to Q_1 must Q_2 be moved to double the potential energy of the system?

Problem: Point charges Q_1 and Q_2 are separated by a distance a. Charge Q_2 is allowed to move to a position distance b away from Q_1. Obtain an expression for the change in potential energy of the system.

The system is illustrated in figure T2.4. Q_2 experiences a force tending to move it away from Q_1 along the line of centres. Let it move to some general point, distance r away from Q_1. The force at that point is given by:

$$F_r = E_r Q_2 = \frac{Q_1}{4\pi\varepsilon_0 r^2} \cdot Q_2 \qquad \text{(T2.9)}$$

Now let it move a small distance δr in the same direction. The small amount of work done by the system in moving this distance is

$$\delta WD = F_r \delta r \qquad \text{(T2.10)}$$

The total work done by the system as Q_1 moves from

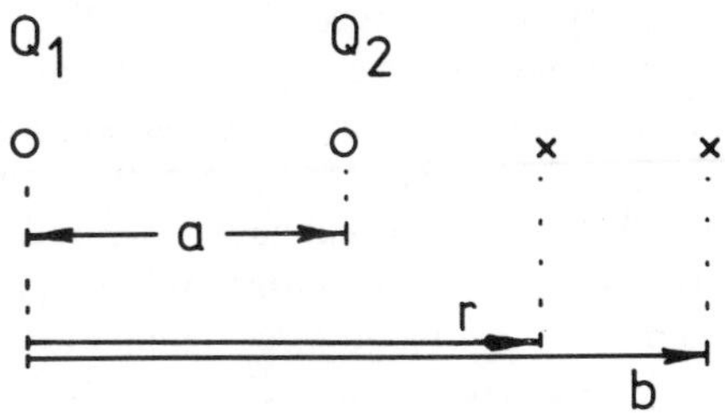

Fig.T2.4

$r = a$ to $r = b$ is:

$$WD = \sum_{r=a}^{r=b} F_r \delta r \qquad \text{(T2.11)}$$

and in the limit as δr becomes very small this equation becomes:

$$WD = \int_{r=a}^{r=b} F_r \, dr = \int_{r=a}^{r=b} \frac{Q_1 Q_2}{4\pi\varepsilon_0 r^2} \, dr = \left[\frac{-Q_1 Q_2}{4\pi\varepsilon_0 r} \right]_a^b$$

Therefore

$$WD = \frac{Q_1 Q_2}{4\pi\varepsilon_0} \left[\frac{1}{a} - \frac{1}{b} \right] \qquad \text{(T2.12)}$$

This work is done by the system, so that its potential energy must have fallen by that amount. Or, if you prefer it, we could say that the potential energy of Q_2 at point a is greater than its potential energy at point b by the amount given in equation T2.12.

Question 12

A point charge of 10^{-6} coulombs is 0.73 metres away from a point charge of 10^{-7} coulombs in a northerly direction. The first charge is now moved to a point 0.73 metres away from the second charge in a southerly direction. What is the change in potential energy of the system?

You should appreciate that the only relevant information in this question is the distance, 0.73 m. As long as the second charge is 0.73 m away from the first there is no energy change. What this means of course is that you can move the second charge from one point on the surface of an imaginary sphere of radius 0.73 m to any other point on that surface without doing any work. The same is true on any sphere of any radius, provided it is concentric with the first charge. We have, in other words, spheres of equipotential about a point charge. There is a parallel here between the electrostatic field about a charged sphere and the gravitational field about a spherical mass. If we consider the earth as approximately spherical, then the potential energy of a body at a given distance from the centre of the earth is the same no matter where, geographically, it may be. The potential energy of a charged sphere, a given distance from the centre of another charged sphere, also remains constant as the first sphere moves about an orbital path of fixed radius. There is another aspect of this worth considering. If there is no change in potential energy in moving from one point to another on an equipotential surface then there can be no force acting along the surface. In general electric field strength must act perpendicularly to an equipotential surface. This is something we might make use of later on.

Now try the self assessment questions at the end.

T2.5   AN EXTENSION

In section T2.3 we defined the electric field strength at a point in space as the force that a unit positive charge would experience if placed at that point. We showed that if the electric field strength were due to a point charge Q distance r away from the point then:

$$E_r = \frac{Q}{4\pi\varepsilon_0 r^2}$$

What we must now recognise is that the case of a point charge is an exceptional one. In electrical engineering we meet charged sheets or charged cylinders far more frequently than we meet small charged spheres. How then can we extend what we have done to these cases? The following example will show how it is done for a flat, charged disc.

Let us then consider a thin, charged disc and let us assume that charge is distributed uniformly over the surface with a surface density of σ.

We have previously talked of small charged spheres and argued that in the limit they behave as point charges. We could also argue that a flat, charged surface would appear as a point charge when seen from a great distance, or that a very small flat surface would appear as a point charge when seen from a point near by. Let us do just that. Let us look upon each minute element of surface area as a point charge and then consider the whole surface as the sum of many such small elements.

One such small surface is shown in figure T2.5.

The small surface area $\delta S = x\delta\theta \,.\, \delta x$
$$= x\delta x \,.\, \delta\theta$$

The charge on this area $= \sigma\,x\,\delta x\,\delta\theta$

We consider this acting at a point in the centre of the area δS. The effect at a point P on the axis of the disc is an electric field strength δE given by:

$$\delta E = \frac{\sigma x\delta x \,.\, \delta\theta}{4\pi\varepsilon_0 r^2} \quad \text{in the direction given}$$

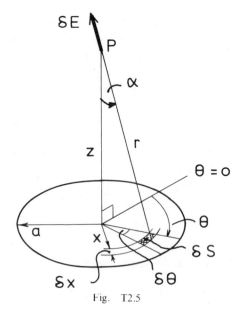

Fig.   T2.5

This is the force that would act on a unit point charge placed at P.

To obtain a solution to the problem we have to work out the resultant effect of all the small areas. The first point to appreciate is that there is a small area δS_2 diametrically opposite to δS which will also produce a component δE at P. It should be clear that the two horizontal components of the two δE vectors will cancel. By symmetry we will only have the vertical components of the δE vectors to sum.

Vertical component of δE

$$= \delta E_z = \frac{\sigma x\delta x\delta\theta}{4\pi\varepsilon_0 r^2}\cos\alpha$$

$$\delta E_z = \frac{\sigma x\delta x\delta\theta}{4\pi\varepsilon_0(x^2+z^2)} \cdot \frac{z}{\sqrt{x^2+z^2}}$$

$$\delta E_z = \frac{\sigma zx\delta x \,.\, \delta\theta}{4\pi\varepsilon_0(x^2+z^2)^{3/2}} \tag{T2.13}$$

Now for the summation. We do this in two parts. First of all we let θ vary from 0 to 2π and add up all the contributions from all the elements of width δx, distance x from the centre. This gives us the resultant electric field at P for a thin ring of charge. We then let x vary from 0 to a and add up all the contributions from all the rings as x changes. Thus:

Summing round the ring $= \displaystyle\sum_{\theta=0}^{\theta=2\pi} \delta E_z$

$$= \sum_{\theta=0}^{\theta=2\pi} \frac{\sigma zx \,.\, \delta x}{4\pi\varepsilon_0(x^2+z^2)^{3/2}} \cdot \delta\theta$$

which in the limit as $\delta\theta \to 0$ becomes:

$$\int_{\theta=0}^{\theta=2\pi} \frac{\sigma zx \,.\, \delta x}{4\pi\varepsilon_0(x^2+z^2)^{3/2}} \cdot d\theta = \frac{\sigma zx \,.\, \delta x}{4\pi\varepsilon_0(x^2+z^2)^{3/2}} \cdot 2\pi \tag{T2.14}$$

Summing for all the rings:

$$\sum_{x=0}^{x=a} E = \sum_{x=0}^{x=a} \cdot \frac{\sigma z 2\pi}{4\pi\varepsilon_0} \cdot \frac{x\delta x}{(x^2+z^2)^{3/2}}$$

which in the limit as $\delta x \to 0$ becomes:

$$\int_{x=0}^{x=a} \frac{\sigma z 2\pi}{4\pi\varepsilon_0} \cdot \frac{x\,dx}{(x^2+z^2)^{3/2}} = \frac{\sigma z 2\pi}{4\pi\varepsilon_0}\left[\frac{-1}{(x^2+z^2)^{1/2}}\right]_{x=0}^{x=a}$$

Therefore

$$E_z = \frac{\delta}{2\varepsilon_0}\left[1 - \frac{z}{\sqrt{z^2+a^2}}\right] \qquad \text{(T2.15)}$$

Notice that the expression for E in equation T2.15 is quite unlike equation T2.2. Obvious though this is, it needs to be pointed out. A very common mistake made by students is to use the equations developed for a point-charge system for solving problems relating to other systems. This is a mistake you can avoid. The expression for E will vary with the geometry of the system of charges. In Task 4 we will develop a method for determining E in all the commonly used arrangements of charged conductors.

T2.6   SELF-ASSESSMENT QUESTIONS

Question 13

The point charges Q_1, Q_2 and Q_3 in figure T2.6 have values $Q_1 = Q_2 = Q_3 = 10^{-6}$ C.

Determine the electric field strength at Q_1 due to Q_2 and Q_3; at Q_2 due to Q_1 and Q_3; and at Q_3 due to Q_1 and Q_2.

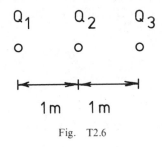

Fig.   T2.6

Question 14

Point charges Q_1 and Q_2 of 10^{-6} C are separated by a distance of 1 m. A third charge Q_3, also of value 10^{-6} C, is brought from infinite to the point midway between

Q_1 and Q_2. How much work has to be done on Q_3 during this movement?

Question 15

Two charges Q_1 and Q_2 are of opposite sign and are initially separated by an infinitely large distance. In this condition the potential energy of the system is defined as zero. Obtain an expression for the potential energy of this system of two charges when they are separated by a distance a.

Question 16

The point charges Q_1, Q_2 and Q_3 in figure T2.6 have values $Q_1 = Q_3 = 10^{-6}$C; $Q_2 = -10^{-6}$C.

Determine the potential energy of this system.

Question 17

A thin circular loop of radius 4 cm carries a total charge of 10^{-11}C distributed uniformly around its circumference. Calculate the electric field strength at a point on the axis of the loop 3 cm above the plane of the loop. NB Read section 2.5 before attempting this question.

Question 18

The electric field strength along the line between the two points A and B in space is given by $E_x = 300\,x$ kVm^{-1}; where x is measured from A along the line AB and E acts positively from A to B. An electron enters the region through the point A with a velocity u along the line AB. It leaves the region at B. The case is illustrated in figure T2.7.

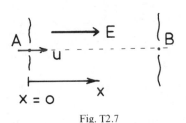

Fig. T2.7

Calculate the change in kinetic energy of the electron as it travels from A to B.

T2.7 SOLUTIONS

1. $F = \dfrac{Q_1 Q_2}{4\pi\varepsilon_0 r^2}$ or $F = 9 \, 10^9 \dfrac{Q_1 Q_2}{r^2}$

2. Force is a vector quantity
3. Electric field strength is a vector

4. E at $Q_2 = \dfrac{Q_1}{4\pi\varepsilon_0 r^2}$

5. $|F|$ on Q_2 due to $Q_3 = \dfrac{Q_2 Q_3}{4\pi\varepsilon_0 r_2^2}$ acting from Q_2 to Q_3.

6. $|F|$ on Q_2 due to $Q_1 = \dfrac{Q_1 Q_2}{4\pi\varepsilon_0 r_1^2}$ acting from Q_2 to Q_3.

7. $|E|$ on Q_2 due to $Q_3 = \dfrac{Q_3}{4\pi\varepsilon_0 r_2^2}$ acting from Q_2 to Q_3.

8. $|E|$ at Q_2 due to $Q_1 = \dfrac{Q_1}{4\pi\varepsilon_0 r_1^2}$ acting from Q_2 to Q_3.

9. $|F_R|$ on $Q_2 = \dfrac{Q_2 Q_3}{4\pi\varepsilon_0 r_2^2} + \dfrac{Q_2 Q_1}{4\pi\varepsilon_0 r_1^2}$ acting from Q_2 to Q_3.

10. $|E_R|$ at $Q_2 = \dfrac{Q_3}{4\pi\varepsilon_0 r_2^2} + \dfrac{Q_1}{4\pi\varepsilon_0 r_1^2}$ acting from Q_2 to Q_3.

11. 0.25 m
12. Zero
13. At Q_1: $E = 11.25 \ 10^{-3}$ V.m^{-1} along the line of centres away from Q_2.
    At Q_2: $E =$ zero
    At Q_3: $E = 11.25 \ 10^{-3}$ V.m^{-1} along the line of centres away from Q_2.
14. When positioned midway between Q_1 and Q_2 the charge Q_3 experiences no resultant electrostatic force. It is in an equilibrium position, but the equilibrium is unstable. Let us therefore displace Q_3 and allow it to move under the action of the forces. It will then move as far as possible away from Q_1 and Q_2, and in so doing it releases its potential energy. This energy has two components: one due to the relative position of Q_3 and Q_1 and the other due to

the relative position of Q_3 and Q_2. We can calculate these separately.

Potential energy of $Q_3 Q_1 = \dfrac{Q_3 Q_1}{4\pi\varepsilon_0} \dfrac{1}{0.5}$ (from equation T2.8)

Potential energy of $Q_3 Q_2 = \dfrac{Q_3 Q_2}{4\pi\varepsilon_0} \dfrac{1}{0.5}$

Total $= 36 \ 10^{-3}$ J
Therefore the work to be done to place Q_3 midway between Q_1 and Q_2 must be $36 \ 10^{-3}$ J.
15. We again make use of equation T2.8, but now Q_1 and Q_2 are of opposite sign so that the potential energy is negative. The system therefore has a lower potential energy when the charges are separated by a distance a than when the charges are an infinite distance apart.
16. Potential energy $= -13.5 \ 10^{-3}$ J with respect to a defined zero of potential energy for which all charges are separated by an infinite distance.
17. $E = 21.6$ V m^{-1}
    If you have difficulty with this, follow through section T2.5 as far as equation T2.14. This is in effect the answer. You need to see the connection between the product $\sigma \cdot x \cdot \delta x$ and the total charge on the ring. From there on it is an arithmetic problem.
18. At a distance x from A towards B, the electric field strength is $300x . 10^3$ Vm^{-1}. The force on the electron at this point is $e \ E = e \ 300x \ 10^3$ Vm^{-1}. As the electron moves a small distance δx towards B, it does work against the force. This element of work done is $e \ E \ \delta x$. The total work done by the electron moving from A to B is

$$\int_0^{5.10^{-2}} e \ 300x . 10^3 \, \mathrm{d}x$$

$$= e \cdot \frac{300x^2}{2} \ 10^3 = 6 \ 10^{-17} \text{ J}$$

The energy to do this work must come from the kinetic energy of the electron. Thus the kinetic energy lost is $6 \ 10^{-17}$ J.

CHAPTER 6

Task 3: Electric potential difference

T3.1 INTRODUCTION

In this section we shall define electric potential difference and examine the relationship between it and electric field strength.

T3.2 OBJECTIVES

When you have finished this task you should be able to do the following:

(a) define the electric potential difference between two points in terms of the work done moving a unit charge between two points;
(b) calculate the change in energy associated with a charge moving through a potential difference;
(c) calculate the potential difference between two points given the electric field strength as a function of the distance along the line joining the two points;
(d) calculate the electric field strength at a point given the spatial variation of the potential about the point; and
(e) answer the self-assessment questions correctly.

T3.3 PRIOR KNOWLEDGE

You should have completed Task 2 and be able to answer the self-assessment questions for that section.

T3.4 ELECTRIC POTENTIAL DIFFERENCE

The previous task was concerned with potential energy in the electrostatic fields produced by point charges. It is useful to be able to describe an electrostatic field in terms of energy because energy is a scalar quantity and the mathematical manipulation of scalar quantities is less complicated than the manipulation of vector quantities. Thus it is sometimes easier to talk in terms of energy than to talk in terms of electric field strength. However, if we are to describe all electrostatic fields in terms of energy we are going to need a defined measure. It must be one which describes the field in a useful way and it must be of general application. The measure we adopt is the ELECTRIC POTENTIAL. It is always measured with respect to some reference point so that it is perhaps better thought of as an electric potential DIFFERENCE. How then do we define electric potential difference?

The electric potential of a point A in space with respect to a reference B is defined as the work done moving a unit charge from point B to point A. The symbol used for potential difference is V, the unit of measurement is the VOLT (V) and 1 volt is equal to 1 joule per coulomb.

Thus if we say that there is a potential difference of 10 volts between two points in space we are in fact saying that moving a unit charge from one point to the other will involve a change in potential energy of the system of 10 joules. If a positive charge is moved from a point of lower potential to a point of higher potential work is done on the system and the energy appears as an increase in the potential energy of the system.

Question 1

Point A has a potential of $+20$ V with respect to point B. How much work must be done to move a positive unit charge from B to A?

Question 2

A positive unit charge moves from a point of higher potential to a point of lower potential. The potential difference is 5 V. What is the change in potential energy of the system?

Question 3

An electron accelerates through a vacuum from a plate at zero potential to a plate at $+5000$ V. How much energy is gained by the electron in this movement? (Take q_e as $1.6 \ 10^{-9}$ C.)

T3.5 THE RELATIONSHIP BETWEEN POTENTIAL AND ELECTRIC FIELD STRENGTH

Suppose we have an electric field strength E acting along a straight line. Let us measure distance x along the line in the direction of E. A positive unit charge placed at a point A on the line will tend to move along the line in the direction of increasing x under the action of E. The work done (WD) by the system as the charge moves from A to B is given by:

$$\text{WD} = \int_A^B E \, \mathrm{d}x \qquad \text{(T3.1)}$$

Now let us push the unit charge back to A. This time work is done on the system against the force due to E and the work done is given by:

$$\text{WD} = -\int_B^A E \, \mathrm{d}x \qquad \text{(T3.2)}$$

But, the work done moving a unit charge from a point B to a point A is defined as the potential of A with respect to B. Thus:

$$V_{AB} = -\int_B^A E \, \mathrm{d}x \qquad \text{(T3.3)}$$

Alternatively,

$$\frac{\mathrm{d}V}{\mathrm{d}x} = -E \qquad \text{(T3.4)}$$

Thus we see that V and E are related. The electric field strength E is sometimes referred to as the potential gradient, or voltage gradient.

Question 4

What is the force acting on a unit charge situated in a uniform field of potential gradient 10 Vm^{-1}?

It is important to note that we have been discussing the action of E along one straight line. In practice E may have components along each of the co-ordinate axes so that there will be a voltage gradient along x, y and z axes. The magnitude of E may also vary along each axis. In general then we should write E as a vector sum of three components, thus:

$$\bar{E} = -\frac{\partial V}{\partial x} \text{ in the } x \text{ direction}$$

$$-\frac{\partial V}{\partial y} \text{ in the } y \text{ direction}$$

$$-\frac{\partial V}{\partial z} \text{ in the } z \text{ direction.}$$

T3.6 SELF-ASSESSMENT QUESTIONS

Question 5

A small conducting sphere S carries a charge of 10^{-12} C. Two other small spheres A and B are placed at points 10 cm and 20 cm away from the first sphere. Initially the three spheres lie along a straight line. Determine the potential of Sphere A with respect to Sphere B.

Sphere A is now moved so that the line through SA is at right angles to the line through SB. The distances SA and SB remain unchanged. What is the potential difference between spheres A and B?

Question 6

Two concentric cylinders form a simple electric cable. In the space between the cylinders the electric field strength acts radially outwards from the central axis. The magnitude of the field strength at any radius r is given by $E_r = q/2\pi\varepsilon_0 r$ where q is the charge on a metre length of the inner cylinder. If the radii of the inner and outer cylinders are 1 cm and 4 cm respectively, calculate the potential of the inner conductor with respect to the outer conductor. Assume $q = 4 \; 10^{-9} \text{ C m}^{-1}$.

Question 7

Two large flat plates are positioned with their flat surfaces parallel. The distance between the plates is 1 cm and a voltage difference of 200 V is maintained between the plates. The electric potential between the plates falls off with distance in the manner shown in figure T3.1. Determine the electric field strength at points in the space between the plates.

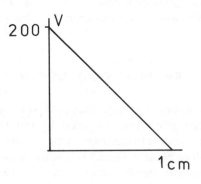

Fig. T3.1

T3.7 ANSWERS AND SOLUTIONS

1. 20 joules (J)
2. -5 J
3. $8 \; 10^{-16}$ J
4. 10 N
5. A common first reaction to this problem is to question whether or not S lies between the spheres A and B. In fact, the alternative positions allowed by the question give the same result. This becomes apparent when we consider precisely what we are doing. The question asks for the potential differences between spheres A and B. Let us be more exact and ask for the potential of sphere A with respect to sphere B. This is the work that we would have to do in moving a positive unit charge from B to A. Now look at the representation in figure T3.2. The electric field about S

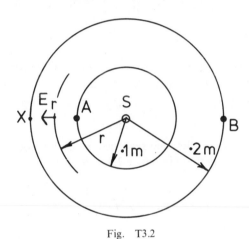

Fig. T3.2

will have a spherical geometry and surfaces of equipotential about S will be spheres centred on S. A section through the field along the line ASB will 'reveal' circular equipotential lines. Two such are shown in figure T3.2, one of radius 10 cm and one of radius 20 cm. We note that point X has the same potential as the sphere at B and we see therefore

that the potential of A with respect to B is equal to the potential of A with respect to X.

The electric field strength between A and X acts from A towards X and has a value $Q/4\pi\varepsilon_0 r^2$ at the radius r.

Thus

$$V_{AB} = V_{AX} = -\int_{0.2}^{0.1} \frac{Q}{4\pi\varepsilon_0 r^2} \, dr = 45 \text{ mV}$$

The answer to the second part of the question is also 45 mV.

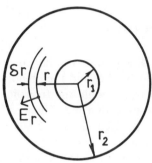

Fig. T3.3

6.

$$V_{AB} = -\int_{r_2}^{r_1} E_r \, dr,$$

where $r_1 = 1$ cm, $r_2 = 4$ cm

We note that E_r is a function of r and we must therefore write

$$V_{AB} = -\int_{r_2}^{r} \frac{q}{2\pi\varepsilon_0 r} \, dr = 100 \text{ V}$$

7. The electric field strength between the plates is constant and has a value equal to the slope of the graph in figure T3.1

$$E = -\frac{dV}{dx} = 20\,000 \text{ V m}^{-1}$$

acting in the sense of increasing x.

CHAPTER 7

Lightning, kugelblitz and when to stand on one leg

7.1 INTRODUCTION

In a heavy rainstorm a cow has an understandable desire to look for shelter and the obvious place to find this is under a tree. Should the tree then be struck by lightning, the cow stands a good chance of being electrocuted. Its basic problem is that it has too many legs, spread too far apart.

If the surface of the tree trunk is smooth and wet, it will present a relatively low-impedance path to the lightning current. This current, which can be tens of thousands of amperes, passes into the earth at the base of the tree and then spreads out in all directions in the top conducting layer of the ground. This sets up a potential gradient along the surface and the cow will find that the foot nearest the tree will be at a higher potential than the foot furthest away from the tree. Clearly a current will flow through the cow from one end to the other.

Should the tree have a very rough bark, as an oak tree does, the conducting path down the trunk may not be complete or it may have a relatively high impedance. One of two things may then happen. The current may divert into the sapwood of the tree and the tree explode, or a flashover may occur between the tree and any nearby conducting object which will then carry the full discharge current.

7.2 POTENTIAL GRADIENTS IN THE GROUND

We can obtain some idea of the magnitude of the potential gradient along the surface of the ground about the point of impact of a lightning stroke by considering the effect about an idealised earth electrode. Consider a hemispherical, conducting electrode buried in earth of resistivity ρ as shown in figure 7.1.

At distance x from the centre of the electrode the current I is spread uniformly over a hemispherical surface of area $2\pi x^2$. If we permit x to increase by an amount δx we will record a change in potential across δx given by

$$\delta V = -I\,\delta R$$

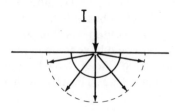

Fig. 7.1

where δV is measured in the sense of x increasing and the change in resistance δR is given by

$$\delta R = \frac{\rho\,\delta x}{2\pi x^2}$$

The potential difference recorded as we go from $x = d_1$ to $x = d_2$, as defined in figure 7.3, will be

$$V_T = -\sum_{x=d_1}^{x=d_2} \frac{I\rho\,\delta x}{2\pi x^2}$$

which becomes

$$V_T = -\int_{d_1}^{d_2} \frac{I\rho\,\mathrm{d}x}{2\pi x^2} = \frac{I\rho}{2\pi}\left[\frac{1}{d_2} - \frac{1}{d_1}\right]$$

Since $d_2 > d_1$, V_T is negative, i.e. the potential change as x increases from d_1 to d_2 is negative or, the potential of the thin shell of radius d_1 is positive with respect to the potential of the thin shell of radius d_2 by a potential difference V where $V = -V_T$.

If we let $I = 10^4$ A, $\rho = 10^2\ \Omega$ m, $d_1 = 2$ m, $d_2 = 3$ m then $V = 26$ kV. This potential difference will exist on the ground surface between the two notional rings of radius d_1 and d_2.

Now suppose that some large distance away the earth remains electrically neutral, i.e. at zero potential,

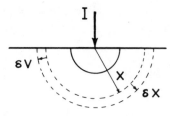

Fig. 7.2

20

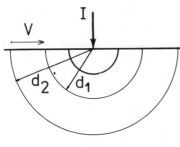

Fig. 7.3

then the potential of the electrode of radius a with respect to the distant region will be:

$$V = \int_a^\infty \frac{I\rho}{2\pi x^2} \, dx = \frac{I\rho}{2\pi} \left[-\frac{1}{\infty} + \frac{1}{a} \right]$$

and if a is one metre, V is 159 kV.

The implications of this are considerable. Suppose lightning strikes a modern, steel-framed building. The potential of the whole structure will increase with respect to true 'earth'. This is fine provided that no point in the building remains at true earth potential, but if a conducting cable runs into the building, and if that cable is earthed only at a remote point, then the full potential difference will appear between the cable and the structure of the building. Any person handling that cable or equipment connected to it will be electrocuted. In fact great care is taken over the earthing of structures and electrical supplies to prevent accidents of this kind.

7.3 THE LIGHTNING DISCHARGE

There have been many theories developed to explain how a thundercloud becomes charged, but none is totally acceptable. The most satisfactory explanation at present is as follows.

Ice particles falling through the cloud collide with super-cooled water droplets. The droplets freeze onto the ice particles causing them to become negatively charged. At the same time, small, positively charged splinters of ice are thrown off. The splinters are light enough to be carried upwards by the strong updraught of air in the cloud whilst the heavier ice particles fall. The nett effect is to charge the upper regions of the cloud positively and the lower region negatively. The total amount of charge involved can be as much as 100 coulombs.

The lightning discharge itself begins in the cloud and extends downwards towards the ground. The first phase of the stroke is called the 'leader stroke' and this is a thin channel of ionised air. At the tip of this channel there is an intense electric field which causes ionisation of the air in front so that the channel can progress. As

the channel approaches the ground, the electric field strength can become so intense that a second discharge will begin at ground level and move upwards to meet the leader. Once a complete ionised channel exists between cloud and ground the main electrical discharge between the two can occur.

7.4 THE CORONA DISCHARGE

We can best approach this phenomenon by examining what happens at the tip of a lightning conductor during a storm. If the cloud base is negatively charged, the induced charge on the conductor and ground will be positive and any electrons in the space around the tip will be attracted towards it. As a first approximation we can assume the tip of the conductor to be hemispherical, as in figure 7.4, and we can then argue that the electric field above the tip is similar to the field about a charged sphere. The electric field strength will then act radially outwards from the centre of the sphere and surfaces of equipotential will be spherical surfaces concentric with the hemisphere. The electric field strength about the tip will obey an inverse-square law and an electron moving into the field will be pulled along a radial flow line and accelerated into a stronger and stronger field.

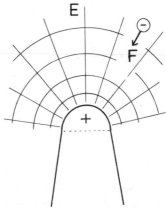

Fig. 7.4

As the electron moves towards the tip it will inevitably collide with an air molecule. If the electron has sufficient energy, it may knock another electron off the molecule leaving a positive ion. The two electrons will then accelerate into the field, collide with two molecules, produce two more electrons and the four electrons can again accelerate towards the tip. The process is cumulative and is described as an electron avalanche. The electrons have a much higher mobility than the positive ions so that they will sweep rapidly into the positive conductor leaving behind a relatively persistent region of positive charge. This positive space charge appears as a conducting extension of the tip and it has two opposing effects. On the one hand it effectively reduces the distance between the positive conductor and the negative cloud base which tends to increase the potential gradient, while on the other hand it makes the effective radius of the tip larger which tends to decrease the electric field strength about the tip. Under certain conditions these effects balance and there is then a fairly stable region of ionised air around the tip maintained by a regular avalanche effect as electrons drift into the region from surrounding space. This is called a corona discharge. It produces light, audio noise, electromagnetic radiation and ozone. It can occur wherever there is a non-uniform electric field of sufficient intensity and not just in thunderstorms. It can be found on high voltage lines and within electrical equipment where close spacing of components causes high field strengths. We have already met applications of it in the electrostatic copier and the precipitator.

7.5 KUGELBLITZ

Scientists call it ball lightning, a journalist might describe it as *Great Balls of Fire*, but perhaps the German word Kugelblitz best fits this mysterious and potentially dangerous phenomenon. It occurs frequently, usually in association with violent storms, and takes the form of a luminous ball with a diameter of the order of 20 cm. Its behaviour is unpredictable. Sometimes it falls to the ground, sometimes it hovers and on occasions it has been seen to rise in the air and float about. Witnesses claim that it has entered premises through open windows and doors and even by way of the chimney. Sometimes it emits sparks, sometimes it crackles, sometimes it is silent and still, like a visiting spirit. It might bring death and destruction or it might disappear without trace.

There is no generally acceptable explanation of ball lightning, indeed some scientists claim that there is no such thing and that all so-called observations are optical illusions. This is difficult to accept in view of the many well-documented sightings, some of which are by reliable and expert witnesses. It would seem that the best explanation of ball lightning so far is that it is a plasma consisting of a gaseous mixture of electrons, positive ions and uncharged molecules, which is confined by electromagnetic fields into a spherical volume. The plasma would be at a high temperature and it would contain a high density of electric charge. One possible mechanism of confinement could be the effect on a moving electron of a magnetic field. If the electron moves across the magnetic field it will experience a force acting in a direction perpendicular to its line of motion and perpendicular to the line of action of the magnetic field. Given the right conditions the electron would proceed around a circular path under the action of this force, and the radius of the path would be determined by the initial velocity of the electron and the strength of the magnetic field.

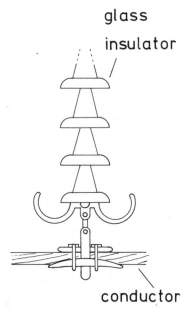

Fig. 7.5

7.6 CONCLUSION

Cows and Kugelblitz may seem far removed from the electrical engineer's world, but the electrical breakdown of air, and gases in general, is a very important phenomenon. The main electrical insulation of overhead transmission lines throughout the world is air. The conductors are bare and are suspended from the arms of large steel towers by glass or ceramic insulators as shown in figure 7.5. The whole arrangement is carefully designed to minimise the possibility of electrical breakdown in the surrounding air. The major concern is with the magnitude of the electric field strength in the air, because it is the electric field that accelerates stray electrons to cause ionisation. Voltage by itself is not enough. What matters is voltage gradient, and in the next Task we shall learn to use a technique which will enable us to calculate electric field strength, or potential gradient, around common geometric arrangements of conductors.

CHAPTER 8

Task 4: Gauss' law

T4.1 SUMMARY

Gauss' law gives us a method by which we can determine the electric field strength about charged bodies with simple geometries. In this Task we shall look at a simple derivation of Gauss' law and then apply it to some typical problems.

T4.2 OBJECTIVES

When you have completed this Task you should be able to do the following:

(a) write down Gauss' law from memory in the form given in equation T4.3;
(b) explain in your own words what Gauss' law means;
(c) derive, using the law, expressions for the electric field strength about charged spheres, charged cylinders and charged plates; and
(d) use the law and the relationship between E and V to solve problems of the type given in the self-assessment questions.

T4.3 PRIOR KNOWLEDGE

You should know that the projection of an area S onto a surface which makes an angle θ with S is given by $S \cos \theta$. You will need to know the formulae for the surface areas of spheres and cylinders and you should be familiar with the ideas contained in the previous Tasks.

T4.4 GAUSS' LAW

We have learned in the previous Tasks that an electric charge exerts an influence on other electric charges and we can express this influence in terms of the quantity we call the electric field strength. This means that if we can calculate or measure the electric field strength in an electrostatic system then we can analyse the system behaviour in terms of the field strength without having

to concern ourselves further with the nature or location of the charge producing the field. Electric field strength is an important parameter in the design of electrical equipment. Electrical insulation will break down if the electric field strength in it exceeds a certain value. The actual breakdown value varies with the type of insulation, but it is the field strength that matters and not voltage. We therefore need to be able to calculate electric field strength. Gauss' law enables us to do this for cases of simple geometry.

Figure T4.1 shows a charge Q surrounded by a surface of arbitrary shape. The small area δs is part of this surface.

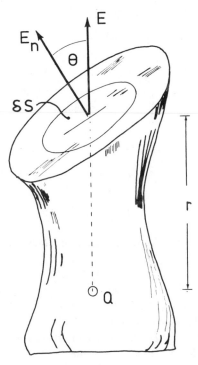

Fig. T4.1

Question 1

Write down the magnitude of the electric field strength at the centre of the area δS distance r from Q.

$$E = \ldots$$

You will recall that E is a vector quantity and the direction of E will be radially outwards from Q. The component of E that is normal to the area δS is $E_n = E \cos \theta$. Now let us write down the product of ε_0, E_n and the elemental area δS. This is:

$$\varepsilon_0 E_n \delta S = \varepsilon_0 E \cos \theta \delta S$$

But $\delta S \cos \theta$ is the projection of δS onto the surface that makes an angle θ with δS or, in other words, it is the projection of δS onto the surface to which E is normal. This is shown in figure T4.2.

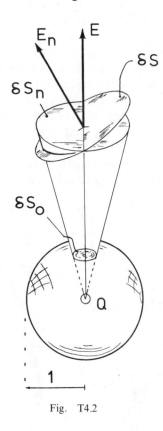

Fig. T4.2

Let $\delta S \cos \theta = \delta S_n$, then $\varepsilon_0 E_n \delta S$ becomes $\varepsilon_0 E \delta S_n$, which is equal to

$$\frac{\delta S_n Q}{4\pi r^2} \tag{T4.1}$$

We now consider the sphere of unit radius centred on point Q. This is shown in figure T4.2. A small portion of the sphere's surface, δS_0, is enclosed by the cone based on δS_n with apex at Q and some simple geometry will show that:

$$\frac{\delta S_0}{(1)^2} = \frac{\delta S_n}{r^2}$$

This enables us to replace r^2 in equation T4.1 giving

$$\varepsilon_0 E_n \delta S = \frac{Q \delta S_0}{4\pi}$$

This equation is for the small element of surface. To obtain an equation for the whole surface we simply add up all the equations for the small elements. This is done by integration, giving

$$\iint_S \varepsilon_0 E_n \, dS = \frac{Q}{4\pi} \iint_{S_0} dS_0 \tag{T4.2}$$

The double integral sign shows that we are summing over a surface. The integral on the right-hand side of equation T4.2 represents the total surface area of the unit sphere S_0. This is clearly equal to $4\pi(1)^2$, which is 4π, so that

$$\iint_S \varepsilon_0 E_n \, dS = Q \tag{T4.3}$$

This is the integral form of Gauss' law. It tells us that if we calculate the product $\varepsilon_0 E_n \, dS$ for each small area on the surface of a closed body, and if we then add up all the contributions from all the small areas we arrive at the value of Q which is the total charge enclosed by the closed body.

We are however still faced with the problem of carrying out the integration of the term $\varepsilon_0 E_n \, dS$ over the surface area. At first sight it appears difficult, but it is possible to simplify the integration in some cases. So much so that the solution becomes trivial. First we should realise that the surface we have been talking about is an arbitrary surface. It can have any shape we choose. Secondly we should understand that we are doing all this so that we can obtain an expression for E at some point in space.

Suppose that we choose a surface over which the value of E_n is constant. How would this help? With E_n constant, equation T4.3 could be written as:

$$\iint_S \varepsilon_0 E_n \, dS = \varepsilon_0 E_n \iint_S dS \tag{T4.4}$$

(remember that ε_0 is also constant).
How do we evaluate the integral in this case? We could try common sense. The summation of all the incremental areas dS over the whole surface must equal the total surface area. So we have

$$\iint_S dS = A$$

the surface area. Therefore

$$\varepsilon_0 E_n A = Q \text{ (from T4.3 and T4.4)}$$

and

$$E_n = \frac{Q}{\varepsilon_0 A} \tag{T4.5}$$

This solution depends on the assumption that E_n is constant all over the surface of integration. So what we have to do when applying Gauss' law in this form is to look for a surface across which the normal component of field strength is constant. The obvious surface is an equipotential surface.

T4.5 APPLICATIONS OF GAUSS' LAW

T4.5.1 The Electric Field About a Long, Straight, Charged Cylinder

We begin by considering a long straight wire with a uniformly distributed charge on its surface of q coulombs per metre length. We want to determine the electric field strength at some point a radial distance r from the axis of the wire. We can use Gauss' law, but we know from the previous section that the easiest way to do this is to find an equipotential surface, so what we really need to know is what the field pattern about a long, straight, charged conductor looks like. This takes us back to Task 1.

The electric force about such a conductor always acts in a radial direction. If we were to look end on to such a conductor we could imagine the lines of action of the electric force radiating out like the spokes of a wheel. The equipotential surfaces are always at right angles to these lines of force so that they must be cylindrical surfaces coaxial with the conductor. We could imagine the field pattern looking something like figure T4.3.

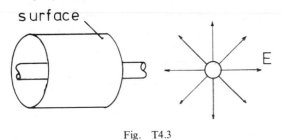

Fig. T4.3

Let us imagine an equipotential cylindrical surface of radius r, and let us apply Gauss' law to it.
We have,

$$\int\int_S \varepsilon_0 E_n \, dS = Q \qquad \text{(T4.6)}$$

and since the surface is an equipotential, $E_n = E$ and E is the same at all points on the surface, therefore,

$$\int\int_S \varepsilon_0 E_n \, dS = \varepsilon_0 E \int\int_S dS \qquad \text{(T4.7)}$$

but,

$$\int\int_S dS = 2\pi r L$$

where L is the length of the cylinder,

therefore

$$\varepsilon_0 E 2\pi r L = Q$$

or

$$E = \frac{Q}{\varepsilon_0 2\pi r L}$$

and since $Q/L = q$

$$E = \frac{q}{\varepsilon_0 2\pi r} \qquad \text{(T4.8)}$$

Question 2

Write down the equation for the electric field strength at the surface of the wire if the wire has a radius a.

Question 3

Sketch a graph showing how the electric field strength varies as the distance from the wire increases.

Question 4

Have we taken into account the whole of the Gaussian surface?

Remember that Gauss' law applies to closed surfaces. We chose a cylinder as our surface and conveniently forgot about the flat ends. We should really add two terms onto equation T4.6, as follows

$$\int\int_S \varepsilon_0 E_n \, dS = \int\int_{\substack{\text{curved} \\ \text{surface}}} \varepsilon_0 E \, dS + \int\int_{\substack{\text{over one} \\ \text{end}}} \varepsilon_0 E_{n1} \, dS + \int\int_{\substack{\text{over the} \\ \text{other end}}} \varepsilon_0 E_{n2} \, dS$$

However, because we have assumed that the electric field strength is everywhere radial, the values of E_{n1} and E_{n2} will both be zero. Our solution is therefore correct. We must be careful though, not to forget about our assumptions. In practice E_{n1} and E_{n2} will not be zero near the ends of cylindrical conductors because of fringing and the assumption is only acceptable near the middle of long conductors. If we were to take a 1 cm length of a 2 cm diameter rod we could not use equation T4.8 to calculate the electric field strength around it, because the assumption of negligible end effects would be totally unjustified.

Question 5

What would be the electric field strength inside a long, straight, charged conductor?

T4.5.2 The Electric Field Above a Large Flat Charged Conducting Plate

Let us assume that the plate has a surface charge

density of σ. The electric force just above the surface will be normal to the surface so that the equipotential surface will lie parallel to the surface of the plate. We choose one of these equipotentials as part of our Gaussian surface. Remember that the Gaussian surface must be closed, so we shall have to add sides of some sort to our flat equipotential surface in order to make something resembling a box. This is illustrated in figure T4.4 and a section through the plate and the box is shown.

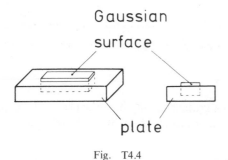

Gaussian

surface

plate

Fig. T4.4

Notice that the sides of the box are perpendicular to the plate. This is deliberately arranged so that these sides will have no component of electric field strength acting across them.

We have,

$$\iint_S \varepsilon_0 E \, dS = Q \tag{T4.9}$$

Since there is no normal component of E across the sides of the box, the integral of $\varepsilon_0 E dS$ over these sides is zero. This leaves only the top and bottom of the box to consider. In your answer to Question 5 you established that there would be no electric field strength at points inside a conductor. This applies equally to the flat conducting plate. If then the bottom of our imaginary box lies within the conducting plate there will be no electric field across it. The only surface left with an electric field across it is the top surface which is part of an equipotential surface. The left-hand side of equation T4.9 becomes, therefore,

$$\iint_A \varepsilon_0 E dS = \varepsilon_0 E \iint_A dS = \varepsilon_0 E A \tag{T4.10}$$

where A is the area of the top of the small box. The right-hand side of equation T4.9 is the charge enclosed by the box. This is equal to σA.

Therefore,

$$\varepsilon_0 E A = \sigma A$$

or

$$E = \frac{\sigma}{\varepsilon_0} \tag{T4.11}$$

Note that the distance of the top of the box from the plate surface does not enter into the solution. Equation T4.11 therefore defines the electric field strength at any point above the plate provided that the equipotential surfaces remain parallel to the plate surface. We could position a second plate above the first, and parallel to it, and equation T4.11 would still hold provided the assumption about the equipotentials remained valid. The assumption would not hold if the plates were separated by distances larger than their linear dimensions. Then T4.11 would only be a rough approximation.

Now try questions 6, 7, 8 and 9 and then come back to section T4.6.

T4.6 ELECTRIC FIELD STRENGTH IN TERMS OF POTENTIAL DIFFERENCE

Equations T4.8 and T4.11 relate electric field strength to the charge on the conductor, but it is more useful to be able to relate E to the potential difference V. The connection between E and V was introduced in Task 3. It is reintroduced here for completeness. Since the basic idea has already been covered, its application may best be seen in a problem solution.

Problem

A simple coaxial cable is made up of a central cylindrical conductor of 5 mm diameter with an outer conducting sheath, also cylindrical, coaxial with the central conductor. The internal diameter of the outer sheath is 20 mm. The space between the two cylinders is empty. Determine the electric field strength at the surface of the inner conductor when the potential difference between the conductors is 500 V.

Solution

We know that E and V are related by the equation

$$V_{AB} = -\int_B^A E \, dr$$

Before we can proceed further we need to know how E varies with r. This is where Gauss' law comes in useful. We have shown, using this law, that the electric field strength at a radius r from the axis of a long cylindrical conductor is given by,

$$E = \frac{q}{2\pi\varepsilon_0 r}$$

Thus the potential difference between the inner and outer conductors of the coaxial cable is given by

$$V_{AB} = -\int_B^A \frac{q}{2\pi\varepsilon_0 r} \, dr \tag{T4.12}$$

The limits of integration will be $B = 10$ mm (the outer radius) and $A = 2.5$ mm (the inner radius).

Thus

$$V_{AB} = - \int_{10\,10^{-3}}^{2.5\,10^{-3}} \frac{q}{2\pi\varepsilon_0} \frac{1}{r} \, dr = \frac{q}{2\pi\varepsilon_0} \ln\left(\frac{10}{2.5}\right) \qquad (T4.13)$$

therefore,

$$q = \frac{2\pi\varepsilon_0 V}{\ln(4)} \qquad (T4.14)$$

Electric field strength at radius r is then given by

$$E_r = \frac{q}{2\pi\varepsilon_0 r} = \frac{V}{r\ln(4)} \qquad (T4.15)$$

The value of E when $r = 2.5$ mm and $V = 500$ V is $144\,10^3$ V m^{-1}. The value of E when $r = 10$ mm and $V = 500$ V is $36\,10^3$ Vm^{-1}. We could of course change the problem around—start with a maximum permissible value of E and determine the maximum voltage that can then be applied across the cable. This can be done using equation T4.15. Now try the remaining questions.

T4.7 SELF-ASSESSMENT QUESTIONS

Question 6

A sphere of conducting material carries a total charge Q and is situated in free space. Use Gauss' law to develop the expression for the electric field strength at a point distance r from the centre of the sphere when r is greater than the sphere radius.

Question 7

Write a short paragraph in your own words explaining what the following equation means

$$\iint_S \varepsilon_0 E_n \, dS = Q$$

Question 8

A large conducting sheet has a uniform surface charge density of 10^{-7} Cm^{-2}. Determine the electric field strength in the space just above the sheet.

Question 9

A simple coaxial cable is made up of a central cylindrical conductor of 5 mm diameter with an outer con-ducting sheath, also cylindrical, coaxial with the central conductor. A charge of 10^{-11} C is held on each metre length of the inner conductor. Determine the electric field strength at a point between the conductors distance 4 mm from the central axis.

Question 10

A cylindrical coaxial cable has an inner conductor of 1 mm diameter and an outer conducting sheath of 10 mm diameter. The volume between the conductors is filled with air. The air will break down electrically if the electric field strength at any point between the conductors exceeds $3\,10^6$ Vm^{-1}.

Determine the maximum voltage that can be applied between inner and outer conductors without breakdown occurring.

Question 11

A sphere of 1 m diameter is isolated in a high-voltage laboratory a considerable distance away from other bodies. If the maximum permissible electric field strength in air is $3\,10^6$ Vm^{-1} determine the maximum charge that the sphere can carry without causing air breakdown, and the potential of the sphere when carrying that charge.

Question 12

The plates of a parallel-plate capacitor are separated by 10 mm. A voltage source of 200 V is connected across the plates. Determine the electric field strength between the plates in vacuum.

Question 13

An ion engine designed for a spacecraft propulsion system works on the following principle.

Caesium ions are emitted with zero velocity from an ionising electrode. They are then accelerated towards a second electrode which is held at a potential of -5000 V with respect to the ioniser. The ions may be assumed to be singly ionised (i.e. only one electron is removed from each). The ions are focused into a parallel beam which then passes through the accelerating electrode. The beam current is $34\,10^{-3}$ A with a current density of 0.1 A cm^2.

It is this ion beam that provides the thrust of the engine. Determine

(a) the value of the electric field strength outside the ion beam after the beam has left the engine, and
(b) the value of the electric field strength within the

ion beam after the beam has left the engine.

You might also consider what reasons there might be for wanting to neutralise the ion beam after it has left the spacecraft.

(Take e/m for caesium as $8 \ 10^3$ C g^{-1}.)

T4.8 ANSWERS AND SOLUTIONS

1. $E = \dfrac{Q}{4\pi\varepsilon_0 r^2}$

2. $E = \dfrac{q}{2\pi\varepsilon_0 a}$

3. See figure T4.5

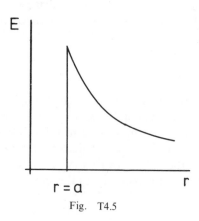

Fig. T4.5

4. No

5. Under electrostatic conditions there can be no electric field strength within a conductor.

6. We look first of all for an equipotential surface over which E is constant. In the case of a charged sphere the equipotential surfaces will be spherical and concentric with the sphere. Let us consider a spherical surface of radius r.

$$\iint_S E\varepsilon_0 \, \mathrm{d}S = Q$$

$$E\varepsilon_0 \iint_S \mathrm{d}S = Q$$

$$E\varepsilon_0 4\pi r^2 = Q$$

$$E = \frac{Q}{4\pi\varepsilon_0 r^2}$$

7. The term $\varepsilon_0 E_n \, \mathrm{d}S$ is the product of the primary electric constant, ε_0, an element of area $\mathrm{d}S$ and the normal component E_n of the electric field strength across the element of area. The sum of the products obtained for all elements $\mathrm{d}S$ of a total closed surface area S is equal to the nett charge enclosed by the surface S.

8. Using equation T4.11, $E = 11.3$ kV.m^{-1}

9. $E = 45$ V.m^{-1}

10. What we are looking for here is a relationship between electric field strength and potential difference. We know that the potential of the inner conductor with respect to the outer conductor may be determined from the equation

$$V = -\int_{r_0}^{r_i} E \, \mathrm{d}r,$$

in which r_i and r_o are the inner and outer radii, but we cannot proceed until we know how E varies with the radius r. This is where Gauss' law helps. For a long, cylindrical system like this the equipotential surfaces are cylinders which are coaxial with the centre conductor. Let us therefore take a general equipotential surface at a radius r, of axial length L, and write:

$$\iint_S \varepsilon_0 E_r \, \mathrm{d}S = Q$$

$$\therefore \varepsilon_0 E_r \iint_S \mathrm{d}S = Q$$

$$\varepsilon_0 E_r 2\pi r L = Q$$

$$E_r = \frac{Q}{\varepsilon_0 2\pi r L}$$

Clearly E_r has a maximum value when r is minimum, which is at the surface of the inner conductor.

$$\therefore E_{max} = \frac{Q}{\varepsilon_0 2\pi \ 0.5 \ 10^{-3} L} = 3.10^6 \text{ Vm}^{-1}$$

and

$$\frac{Q}{\varepsilon_0 2\pi L} = 1.5 \ 10^3$$

Now,

$$V = \int_{0.5 \ 10^{-3}}^{5 \ 10^{-3}} E_r \, \mathrm{d}r = \int_{0.5 \ 10^{-3}}^{5 \ 10^{-3}} \frac{Q}{\varepsilon_0 2\pi r L} \, \mathrm{d}r$$

so that

$$V = \frac{Q}{\varepsilon_0 2\pi L} \ln 10 = 3.45 \text{ kV}$$

11. The fact that the sphere is 'isolated . . . a considerable distance away from other bodies' means that the field close to the sphere will have spherical symmetry. If we assume that the nearest bodies are far enough away to have no significant effect at all on the field about the sphere then we can assume that the field has spherical symmetry everywhere. In fact it then appears as if the sphere were surrounded by another earthed sphere of infinite radius.

E at radius r from the centre of the sphere is given by $Q/\varepsilon_0 4\pi r^2$ provided r is greater than the sphere radius

$$\therefore E_{max} = \frac{Q}{\varepsilon_0 4\pi (0.5)^2} = 3 \ 10^6 \text{ Vm}^{-1}$$

$$\therefore Q = 83.3 \ \mu C$$

The potential of the 1 m sphere with respect to the earthed sphere of infinite radius is given by

$$V = -\int_{\infty}^{0.5} E_r \, dr = -\int_{\infty}^{0.5} \frac{Q}{\varepsilon_0 4\pi r^2} \, dr$$

$$V = \frac{Q}{\varepsilon_0 4\pi} \left[\frac{1}{r} \right]_{\infty}^{0.5}$$

$$V = 1.5 \text{ MV}$$

12. $E = 20 \text{ kV m}^{-1}$

13. The ion engine is represented in figure T4.6 with

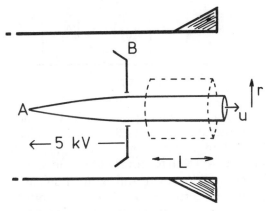

Fig. T4.6

the ioniser at A, the accelerating electrode at B and the beam emerging to the right of B with constant velocity v. On the assumption that the beam takes the form of a parallel cylinder of charge of radius a we can assume that the electric field around the beam has a cylindrical geometry and in particular that equipotential surfaces are cylinders which are coaxial with the axis of the beam. A length L of one such surface of radius r is shown and by applying Gauss' law to the volume enclosed by the surface we obtain:

$$\iint \varepsilon_0 E_r \, dS = Q = \text{charge enclosed by the Gaussian surface shown}$$

or

$$E_r = \frac{1}{2\pi\varepsilon_0 r} \left[\frac{Q}{L} \right]$$

To find E at radius r we need to know Q/L. We know that the charge is moving with a constant velocity v, achieved after acceleration from rest through a potential difference of 5000 V, and equating kinetic energy gained to potential energy lost we have

$$\tfrac{1}{2} mv^2 = eV$$

or

$$v = \sqrt{\left(2V \frac{e}{m} \right)}$$

At constant velocity v, the charge Q enclosed in the Gaussian surface at $t = 0$ will sweep past the end of the tube in a time t, given by

$$t = \frac{L}{v}$$

The current flow, which we know, is

$$I = \frac{Q}{t} = \frac{Qv}{L}$$

$$\therefore \frac{Q}{L} = \frac{I}{v}$$

so that

$$E_r = \frac{1}{2\pi\varepsilon_0 r} \cdot \frac{I}{v}$$

for $r > a$. We can use the same method of analysis for E_r when $r < a$, but as r becomes less than a the charge enclosed by the Gaussian surface reduces to the value

$$Q_1 = \frac{Q}{\pi a^2 L} \pi r^2 L = Q \frac{r}{a^2}$$

$$\therefore E_r = \frac{r}{2\pi\varepsilon_0 a^2} \cdot \frac{I}{v}$$

for $r < a$.

Without neutralisation, the spacecraft becomes electrically changed. The engine then works less efficiently and if the craft comes into contact with another charged object there is the possibility of an electric discharge occurring between them.

CHAPTER 9

Motors and rockets

9.1 INTRODUCTION

Interest in electrostatic motors has recently revived
as a result of developments in space technology and
trends towards miniaturisation. Under normal circumstances the electrostatic machine cannot compete with
the electromagnetic machine because its performance is
limited by the electric breakdown of materials. The
power produced by either type of machine is related to
the energy that can be stored in their respective electromagnetic fields. For the electrostatic motor this is a
function of $\varepsilon_0 E^2$ and for the electromagnetic motor it is a
function of B^2/μ_0, where B is the magnetic flux density
and μ_0 is the permeability of free space. To produce the
same power from machines of similar geometry we must
have $\varepsilon_0 E^2 = B^2/\mu_0$. An acceptable working value for B
is 1 tesla, μ_0 is $4\pi\ 10^{-7}$ H m^{-1} and E then has to be of
the order of $3\ 10^8$ V m^{-1}. Air at normal temperature
and pressure will break down electrically when the
electric field strength exceeds $3\ 10^6$ V m^{-1}. Even
working at this critical value the energy storage in the
electrostatic machine would be a factor of 10^{-4} down
on that for the electromagnetic machine.

Why, then, can we justify the development of electrostatic motors?

In the first case, space operation and operation under
high vacuum improve the relative position of the
electrostatic machine because the breakdown strength
of vacuum is of the order of $3\ 10^8$ V m^{-1}. Secondly,
electrostatic motors are very efficient. Energy losses are
due only to charge transport between and within
electrodes and dielectric losses. This is vitally important
where the source of energy is limited, as in operation
by dry cells or solar cells.

9.2 THE SYNCHRONOUS ELECTROSTATIC MOTOR

The diagram of figure 9.1 represents a portion of two
long strips of steel which have been stamped into the
shape shown. The upper strip is fixed and the lower one
is free to move to left or right. Let the upper strip be

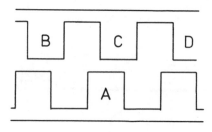

Fig.   9.1

charged positively with respect to the lower. The pole A
will be attracted by the poles B, C and D, but because C
is the closest to A its effect on A will be greatest, thus the
bottom strip will tend to move until A is directly beneath
C. In this position there will be no resultant lateral
component of force on A. Should the bottom strip
move past this position, because of its inertia, it will be
pulled back again, so the tendency is for A to lock into
position under C. A similar argument applies to all
the poles on the bottom strip and clearly this is not a
satisfactory design for a motor.

But, suppose we apply a potential difference between
the two strips which is time-varying in the manner shown
in figure 9.2. There will now be one correct speed at

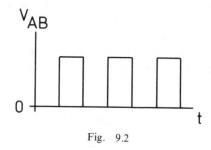

Fig.   9.2

which the machine will produce a nett force. At this
speed poles such as A and C will be attracted during the
period of positive potential difference and will come
directly in line with each other as the potential difference
falls to zero. For the ensuing time period, when the
potential difference remains zero, the bottom strip will
continue moving to the right because of its inertia. As
the potential difference is re-established, pole A will

come under the influence of pole *D* and will be pulled further to the right. The machine will move on one pole pitch for each positive pulse. This is its synchronous speed. What the machine will not do is start, so some kind of starting mechanism will be required.

Obviously the machine does not have to be linear. By wrapping the toothed strips into a disc, or cylinder, we can achieve a traditional rotary machine geometry as illustrated in figure 9.3. You may care to consider

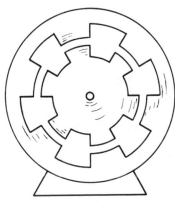

Fig. 9.3

whether or not the machine will work with the voltage waveforms of figures 9.4 and 9.5 applied, and whether or not it can reverse its direction of rotation.

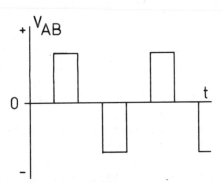

Fig. 9.4

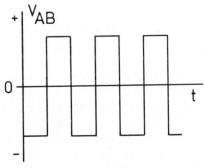

Fig. 9.5

9.3 THE ELECTROSTATIC INDUCTION MOTOR

If an electrically insulating material is placed in an electric field the charge in the material is affected by the field. In a perfect insulator there will be no charge flow, i.e. no electric current, but the distribution of charge within the material may be significantly modified. Figure 9.6 illustrates the result of this for one particular

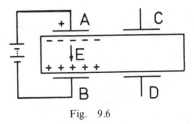

Fig. 9.6

case. The insulating slab between the charged plates *A* and *B* polarises and the top and bottom surfaces appear to have distributed charges on them. Let us now switch the potential difference between *A* and *B* to zero and at the same time make *C* positive with respect to *D*. The charge on the insulator surface will remain where it is for a time because of the low conductivity of the material and during this period it will be attracted towards plates *C* and *D*. The charge is tightly bound to the structure of the material so that the force acting on the charge will be transferred to the material and the slab will tend to move to the right.

Instead of switching the potential difference on and off we could just slide plates *A* and *B* to the right and the slab would follow after them. This gives us the clue to the final solution because in moving the plates to the right we could argue that we are simply moving the

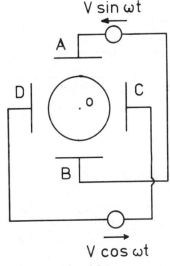

Fig. 9.7

electric field, represented by E, to the right. What is needed then is a moving field system which requires no movement of the electrode system. This can be achieved with the two-phase arrangement of figure 9.7. In this the plates A, B, C and D are fixed and are excited by time-varying voltages $V_{AB} = V \sin \omega t$ and $V_{CD} = V \cos \omega t$. At $t = 0$, $V_{AB} = 0$, $V_{CD} = V$ and the resultant electric field strength acts across the gap from C towards D. At $\omega t = \pi/2$, $V_{CD} = 0$, $V_{AB} = V$ and the resultant electric field strength acts across the gap from A towards B. By extending this argument one can demonstrate that the E vector is effectively rotating anticlockwise in space about the point O. A disc of insulating material centred on O, as illustrated, will also tend to rotate in an anticlockwise direction. In this case the rotor cannot move at the same speed as the field. If it did, it would be as if the charges shown in figure 9.6 remain fixed relative to the plates A and B. This would not produce a lateral force. If the machine were moving, there would be no force to counteract friction so it would slow down. As it slowed, the charge distribution would slip outside the region of the charged plates and there would then be a resultant lateral force tending to pull it back. The velocity of the moving part must, therefore, always be less than the velocity of the field.

9.4 THE CORONA MOTOR

The essential difference between the corona motor and the induction motor is in the method by which the surface charge is established on the rotor. In the induction motor the charge is produced by electrostatic induction. In the corona motor the charge is produced by a corona discharge. A simple linear version of the machine is represented in figure 9.8. Knife-edged

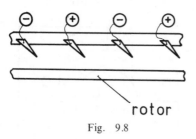

Fig. 9.8

electrodes are mounted on a rigid insulating support and connected to a high-voltage, d.c. supply so that adjacent electrodes are of opposite polarity. The moving part of the machine is a sheet of insulating material. If the electric field strength in the air around the knife edges exceeds the breakdown strength of air a corona discharge occurs and free electrons and ions are pro-

duced. These will move through the resultant electric field following the flow lines. For the geometry of figure 9.8 we could expect the flow lines to be approximately as shown in figure 9.9. In practice it is not quite so

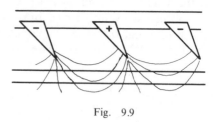

Fig. 9.9

simple because the high density of free charges will itself influence the field pattern. Nonetheless we can see that the general effect will be that some free charge will tend to move onto the surface of the insulating sheet. There it will stick and the force on it will be transferred to the body of the sheet. If the sheet is constrained so that it can only move laterally, i.e. to left or right, only the lateral component of force will be of significance. To make the motor most effective this force has to be maximised. This can be done by careful arrangement of the electrode geometry and by placing a conducting sheet behind the insulating sheet.

A simple rotary version of this machine can be built using a 15 cm length of 7.5 cm diameter plastic tube as the rotor with twelve sharp, metal blades set into the stator frame at an angle of about 30° to the radius. Obviously the frame itself has to be insulating. A machine of these dimensions should work quite well off a 10 kV d.c. supply and with good bearings and a light construction speeds in excess of 3000 r.p.m. should be possible. The power output is low, typically less than 5 W, but efficiencies are high.

On the basis that action does not occur without reaction we can expect a force to be exerted on the stator. If it were possible to lock the rotor and leave the stator free to rotate then the stator would spin in the opposite direction to normal rotor movement. Most of this effect could be attributed to the interaction of the charges present on the stator and the rotor, but a small part of the force on the stator can be seen as a direct thrust due to the ejection of mass in the form of electronic and ionic emission. This takes us back to the original corona machines which were built in 1750 and which were simply very light metal strips pivoted on needles with the ends bent around in the manner shown in figure 9.10. The metal strips rotated when the needles were connected to a high-voltage supply. Simple though the idea is, this principle leads to a new technology—the development of electrostatic rockets for spacecraft.

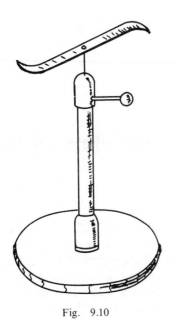

Fig. 9.10

9.5 ELECTRIC PROPULSION FOR SPACECRAFT

Electric rockets for space propulsion are basically reaction-type engines in which the thrust is developed by the controlled emission of mass. This is achieved by expelling a plasma or an ion gas at high velocity from the rocket. In the ion rocket the ion gas is produced by ionising caesium on a hot, tungsten plate, typically at 2200 K. The ion gas is then focused through an electrostatic lens and accelerated through a high potential gradient emerging as a parallel beam of ions at high velocity. Propellant velocities as high as 100 000 mph can be achieved with ion beams and this has to be compared with the propellant velocities of thermal rockets which would usually be less than 25 000 mph. Since the power output is proportional to the square of the propellant velocity it would seem that the electric rocket has a considerable advantage, but when we look at the problem more closely we find that this is not so. The difficulty with the electric rocket is that we have to provide the output energy through the accelerating electric field. In a large electric rocket the energy for this would almost certainly come from a nuclear source and the mass of the energy supply system would far exceed the mass of the equivalent thermal rocket system. The difference in performance is startling. The mass required

to produce a thrust of 1 N from an electric rocket is estimated at about 5000 kg, the equivalent for a thermal rocket is 0.02 kg. The real advantage of the electric rocket comes in law thrust applications, as in interplanetary travel or in attitude correction for space satellites, and here the advantages have been thought sufficient to justify substantial research on the development of ion engines.

In the system layout shown in figure 9.11 there is an

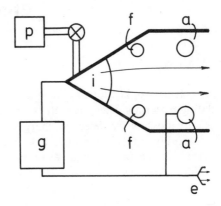

p - propellant
i - ion source
f - focusing
a - accelerator
e - electron gun
g - power supply

Fig. 9.11

electron emitter. This is necessary because the ion beam is positively charged and the continuous emission of positive charge would inevitably lead to a spacecraft with a high negative charge. This would affect the efficiency of the rocket and in the limit could stop it functioning. The emission of electrons from the rocket keeps the rocket electrically neutral.

FURTHER READING

Rocket Propulsion Elements, G. P. Sutton, J. Wiley & Sons, 1967, Chapter 15.

CHAPTER 10

Task 5: The effect of dielectric materials on the electrostatic field

T5.1 SUMMARY

In most electrical applications we have to make use of solid insulating materials. These insulators, or dielectrics, do not usually possess free electric charges, but they nonetheless modify any electrostatic field into which they are placed. In this task we shall examine the mechanism by which dielectrics influence electric fields and we shall show how to modify our previous theories to allow for these effects. Following this we shall consider the concepts of electric flux and electric flux density both of which are useful in situations where we have more than one dielectric present.

T5.2 OBJECTIVES

When you have completed this Task you should be able to do the following:

(a) explain in your own words what is meant by polarisation;
(b) distinguish between relative permittivity and the permittivity of free space;
(c) determine the electric field strength between parallel charged plates and about charged spherical and cylindrical conductors encased in dielectrics;
(d) define relative permittivity in terms of free charge and polarising charge;
(e) define electric flux density in terms of ε_0, ε_r and E;
(f) explain in your own words the concept of electric flux; and
(g) use the principle of continuity of electric flux in the solution of problems involving dielectrics in series.

T5.3 POLARISATION OF DIELECTRICS IN AN ELECTRIC FIELD

If we place a slab of dielectric in an electrostatic field

the electrons in the field will be influenced by the field. The electrons are not free to move through the dielectric so that there will be no current flow, but the motion of the electrons about their atomic nuclei will be modified. Figure T5.1 shows a slab of dielectric containing an electron e within an electric field E.

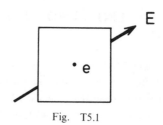

Fig. T5.1

Question 1

In which direction will the electron tend to move under the influence of E?

In the dielectric of figure T5.2 the slight displacement of the electronic orbits is considered to be equivalent to an electronic charge on the top surface and a positive charge on the bottom surface.

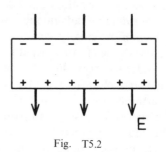

Fig. T5.2

Question 2

Has there been any nett change in the charge balance within the slab?

The dielectric represented in figure T5.2 is said to be

polarised. We can get an indication from figure T5.2 of the way in which the dielectric itself modifies the electrostatic field. Consider an imaginary, exploratory, positive unit charge placed inside the dielectric. What forces will act upon it? It will obviously be influenced by the external field E and will tend to move in the direction of E, but it will also be influenced by the two layers of charge that appear to lie on the top and bottom surfaces of the slab. These will tend to force the unit charge upwards against the direction of E. Thus the total electric field strength within the dielectric, measured as the force acting on a unit charge, will be modified by the charge on the dielectric surface.

T5.4 RELATIVE PERMITTIVITY

Let us take the case of two parallel conducting sheets, charged to opposite polarity with charges of equal magnitude spread uniformly over their surfaces. Let us completely fill the space between the plates with a dielectric medium. The case is represented in figure T5.3.

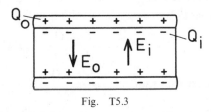

Fig. T5.3

The electric field strength within the dielectric has two components: E_o due to the charge Q_o and E_i due to the polarising charge Q_i on the dielectric surfaces. The resultant, E_R, is given by:

$$E_R = E_o - E_i$$

but,

$$E_o = \frac{Q_o}{\varepsilon_0 A}$$

and

$$E_i = \frac{Q_i}{\varepsilon_0 A}$$

$$\therefore E_r = \frac{(Q_o - Q_i)}{\varepsilon_0 A}$$

where A is the plate area.

We can arrange this as follows:

$$E_R = \frac{(Q_o - Q_i)}{\varepsilon_0 A} = \frac{(Q_o - Q_i)Q_o}{Q_o \varepsilon_0 A} = \frac{Q_o}{\varepsilon_r \varepsilon_0 A} \quad \text{(T5.1)}$$

where ε_r is defined as

$$\frac{Q_o}{Q_o - Q_i} \quad \text{(T5.2)}$$

What we have done is to account for the effect of the polarising charge Q_i by introducing a new factor ε_r.

This factor is called the relative permittivity or dielectric constant. It is a ratio and the value is different for different dielectrics. For transformer oil it is approximately 2.2, for polystyrene 2.6, Nylon 3.5 and mica 6.25. The value can be found experimentally from measurement of capacitance, but we shall look at that in the next Task.

In general if we are examining electrostatic conditions within a homogeneous dielectric we can use the formulae that were derived in the previous Tasks and simply replace ε_0, where it appears, by the product $\varepsilon_0 \varepsilon_r$. The product is called the permittivity of the dielectric and it has the same units and dimensions as ε_0 the permittivity of free space.

Question 3

A large, flat, thin conducting sheet carries a surface charge density of 10^{-6} Cm^{-2}. A slab of dielectric is placed on top of the sheet so that there is no space between them. The relative permittivity of the dielectric is 4. Calculate the electric field strength in the dielectric immediately above the conducting sheet.

Question 4

The electric field strength at a point near a long, straight, cylindrical conductor placed in air is found to be 300 Vm^{-1}. If the whole region is now filled with transformer oil of dielectric constant 2.2 determine the value of the electric field strength at the point if the charge on the conductor remains constant.

T5.5 A SHORT STORY AND A PROBLEM

Once upon a time there was a bright young student who built an air-spaced capacitor as part of a high-voltage project. The student used a parallel plate construction and carefully shaped the edges of the plates so that there were no sharp edges from which discharges could occur. All went well until one day it became necessary to raise the voltage across the plates to some new value. A quick calculation showed that this new voltage difference would produce an electric field strength of 2.8 MV m^{-1} in the air between the plates. The student knew that the theoretical breakdown strength of air was 3 MV m^{-1} and felt, rightly, that he needed to increase his safety margin. 'What I must do', he thought, 'is to increase the breakdown strength of the gap'. This he attempted to do by placing a sheet of Nylon between the plates. The Nylon was only half the thickness of the gap, but he said that this did not matter because Nylon had a much higher breakdown strength than air. He switched on his apparatus, increased the voltage and, to his surprise, the air gap in the capacitor broke down.

Where did he go wrong?

T5.6 ELECTRIC FLUX

So far in this Task we have considered effects in a uniform field between parallel, charged plates. Let us now change our geometry and consider a charge Q uniformly spread over the surface of a small, conducting sphere of radius r_1 which is buried in an insulating sphere of radius r_2 and relative permittivity ε_1. The larger sphere is in turn enclosed in a still larger sphere of insulating material of relative permittivity ε_2. All spheres are concentric, as shown in figure T5.4.

The charge Q causes polarization in the two dielectrics. The electric field strength at a general radius r from the centre is obtained by applying Gauss' law and is given by:

$$E_r = \frac{(Q-Q_1)}{4\pi r^2 \varepsilon_0} = \frac{Q}{4\pi r^2 \varepsilon_0}\left(\frac{Q-Q_1}{Q}\right)$$

where Q_1 is the polarisation charge on the inner surface of the sphere of relative permittivity ε_1, and from our definition of ε_r in equation T5.2 we can recognise $(Q-Q_1)/Q$ as $1/\varepsilon_1$.

We can therefore write:

$$E_r = \frac{Q}{4\pi r^2 \varepsilon_0 \varepsilon_1} \qquad \text{(T5.3)}$$

At a radius r_3, where $r_3 > r_2$, we have:

$$E_r = \frac{(Q-Q_2)}{4\pi r_3^2 \varepsilon_0} = \frac{Q}{4\pi r_3^2 \varepsilon_0 \varepsilon_2} \qquad \text{(T5.4)}$$

where Q_2 is the polarisation charge on the inner surface of the sphere of relative permittivity ε_2. (Note that Gauss' law uses the NETT or resultant charge enclosed by a surface.) It is clear that equations T5.3 and T5.4 are not equal. The electric field strength varies inversely with the square of the radius, because of the geometry, and it changes abruptly with the change in permittivity. But suppose we rewrite the equations as follows:

$$E_r = \frac{Q}{4\pi r^2 \varepsilon_0 \varepsilon_1}$$

and

$$E_{r_3} = \frac{Q}{4\pi r_3^2 \varepsilon_0 \varepsilon_2}$$

so that

$$E_r \varepsilon_0 \varepsilon_1 = \frac{Q}{4\pi r^2}$$

and

$$E_{r_3} \varepsilon_0 \varepsilon_2 = \frac{Q}{4\pi r_3^2}$$

In each case we find that the product $E\varepsilon_0\varepsilon$ gives us a charge density and in each case it is the value we would obtain if we considered the charge Q spread uniformly over the equipotential surface going through the point of interest. In this example both surfaces are spheres, one of radius r, the other of radius r_3. To make the model easier to comprehend let us imagine that the charge Q gives rise to a flow, or flux, which we denote by ψ, and let us imagine that this flow of electric flux spreads out uniformly following the flow lines of the electrostatic field. If we then say that $\psi = Q$ we have equations for flux (or flow) density given by:

$$\frac{\psi}{A} = \frac{Q}{4\pi r^2}$$

and

$$\frac{\psi}{A_3} = \frac{Q}{4\pi r_3^2}$$

where A represents surface area.

The flux ψ is common to both spheres, i.e. the flux that flows out of the inner sphere must flow into the outer sphere. The flux is continuous across the boundary. We can usefully denote the flux density by a particular symbol D so that:

$$D \text{ at radius } r = \frac{\Psi}{A} = \frac{Q}{4\pi r^2} = \varepsilon_0 \varepsilon_1 E_r \quad \text{(T5.5)}$$

$$\text{and } D \text{ at radius } r_3 = \frac{\Psi}{A_3} = \frac{Q}{4\pi r_3^2} = \varepsilon_0 \varepsilon_2 E_r \quad \text{(T5.6)}$$

This defines the well known general relationship $D = \varepsilon_0 \varepsilon_r E$ or $D = \varepsilon_0 E$ in free space. The units of D are coulombs per square metre.

Note that there is no such thing as electric flux, any more than there are such things as lines of force or flow lines. All these things are inventions of our own which we use to explain complex natural phenomena.

Question 5

Does the electric flux density change as we move across from one plate of a parallel plate capacitor to the other?

T5.7 FLUX DENSITY IN A CYLINDRICAL SYSTEM

It is perhaps useful to see the ideas introduced in the previous sections used in a different field geometry. Consider then a long, straight, cylindrical conductor of radius a totally enclosed in a very large block of insulation that has a dielectric constant ε_r. From equation T4.8 we have an expression for E at a general radius r from the axis of the conductor and from this we obtain,

$$E_r = \frac{Q}{2\pi r L \varepsilon_0 \varepsilon_r}$$

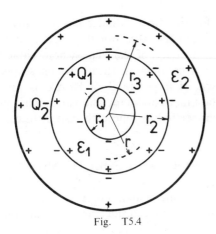

Fig. T5.4

so that

$$D_r = \frac{Q}{2\pi rL}$$

As the area of the imagined Gaussian surface $(2\pi rL)$ gets bigger, D gets smaller. The flux crossing the surface remains constant:

$$\psi = Q = D_r 2\pi rL$$

As an example, consider a cylindrical cable with a 2mm diameter central conductor around which there is a 1 mm thickness of Nylon ($\varepsilon_r = 3.5$). Polythene tape, of relative permittivity 2.3, is wrapped evenly and tightly around the Nylon to a depth of 1 mm. Around the whole there is an outer conducting sheath. The voltage between the inner and outer conductors is 1000 V. Plot graphs showing the variation of the electric field strength and the flux density with varying radius r for values of r between zero and 3 mm.

This is a case of mixed dielectrics and we can make immediate use of our knowledge that the electric flux is continuous. Assume that the total charge on the cable is Q, then $Q = \psi$ and it follows that

$$D = \frac{Q}{2\pi rL}$$

Once we have worked out the value of Q/L we can plot D as a continuous function from $r = 1$ mm to $r = 3$ mm (for $r < 1$ mm, $D = 0$). In the Nylon,

$$E_n = \frac{D}{\varepsilon_0 \varepsilon_n} = \frac{Q}{\varepsilon_0 \varepsilon_n 2\pi rL}$$

and this will have maximum and minimum values at $r = 1$ mm and $r = 2$ mm respectively.

In the polythene,

$$E_p = \frac{Q}{\varepsilon_0 \varepsilon_p 2\pi rL}$$

and this will have maximum and minimum values at $r = 2$ mm and $r = 3$ mm respectively.

In order to calculate Q/L we note that the potential of the inner conductor with respect to the outer sheath is 1000 V. This we can relate to the electric field strength as follows:

$$-\int_{3\,10^{-3}}^{2\,10^{-3}} E_p \, dr - \int_{2\,10^{-3}}^{10^{-3}} E_n \, dr = 1000$$

from which $Q/L = 0.15\ 10^{-6}\ \mathrm{Cm}^{-1}$.

You can now calculate the values of E and D for yourself and plot your results on Figs T5.5 and T5.6.

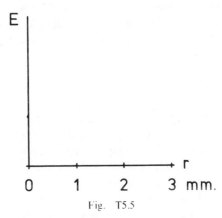

Fig. T5.5

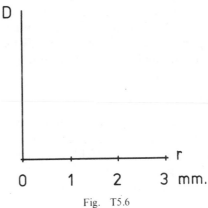

Fig. T5.6

T5.8 SELF-ASSESSMENT QUESTIONS

Question 6

A parallel plate capacitor has a plate separation of 3 mm. The space between the plates is completely filled with two slabs of insulation placed one on top of the other and parallel to the surfaces of the plates. One slab is Nylon, 2 mm thick, with a relative permittivity of 3.6 and the other slab is polythene with a relative permittivity of 2.4. A potential difference of 500 V is maintained across the plates. Determine the electric field strength in each of the dielectrics.

Question 7

The dielectric in a parallel plate capacitor is mica.

The mica is 1 mm thick and completely fills the space between plates. Its electric breakdown strength is $50 \ 10^6 \ Vm^{-1}$. Determine the potential difference across the capacitor for electrical breakdown to occur.

Question 8

A capacitor similar to the one described in the previous question is made, but an airgap of 0.1 mm is left between one surface of the mica and the adjacent parallel plate. Given that the breakdown strength of air is $3 \ 10^6 V \ m^{-1}$ determine the potential difference across the capacitor for an electrical discharge to occur. Take ε_r for mica as 6.0.

Question 9

A conducting sphere of 10 cm diameter is encased in a spherical polythene cover which has a wall thickness of 2 cm. There is no airgap between the polythene and the sphere. The whole is immersed in an oil tank which is large enough for the sides of the tank to have no significant effect on the distribution of the electrostatic field about the sphere. The dielectric constants of the polythene and the oil are 2.4 and 2.0 respectively. The conducting sphere is raised to a potential of 200 kV with respect to the tank walls. Determine the maximum electric field strength in the oil and in the polythene.

Question 10

A parallel-plate, air-filled capacitor is connected to a source of constant voltage. The electric field strength between the plates is then 50 kV m^{-1}. The plate area is 25 cm². The space between the plates is now filled with a dielectric of relative permittivity 4.0. Determine the following:

   (i) the resultant electric field strength in the dielectric;
   (ii) the charge on the plates of the capacitor;
   (iii) the polarisation charge at the surface of the dielectric;
   (iv) the electric field strength in the dielectric due to the polarisation charge.

Question 11

An electric cable is made up as follows: a cylinder of oil-impregnated paper of thickness 0.8 cm is wrapped tightly around a cylindrical conductor of radius 0.8 cm. A thin layer of copper foil is wrapped around the paper and on top of this a second layer of paper is wound to a depth of 0.8 cm. Two different grades of paper are used;

the paper for the inner cylinder has a relative permittivity of 2.4 and the paper for the outer cylinder has a relative permittivity of 2.6. The whole cable is now wrapped in a conducting sheath which serves as the earth return. If a potential of 80 kV is maintained between the inner conductor and earth, what potential does the copper foil assume with respect to earth?

T5.9 ANSWERS AND SOLUTIONS

1. Against the line of action of E.
2. Any small volume inside the slab will contain the same amount of charge as before and this should consist of equal quantities of positive and negative charge.
3. $E = 28.2 \ 10^3 \ V \ m^{-1}$
4. For the conductor in air,

$$E_{air} = \frac{Q}{2\pi r L \varepsilon_0} = 300 \ V \ m^{-1}$$

For the conductor in oil, assuming a polarisation charge Q_1 adjacent to the conductor

$$E_{oil} = \frac{(Q-Q_1)}{2\pi r L \varepsilon_0} = \frac{Q}{2\pi r L \varepsilon_0} \cdot \frac{(Q-Q_1)}{Q} = \frac{Q}{2\pi r L \varepsilon_0} \cdot \frac{1}{\varepsilon_1}$$

$$E_{oil} = E_{air} \cdot \frac{1}{\varepsilon_1} = 137 \ Vm^{-1}$$

(Note that if E has changed and the geometry has stayed the same, then the potential of the conductor must have changed.)

5. No
6. $E = 143 \ 10^3 \ Vm^{-1}$ in the Nylon
   $E = 214 \ 10^3 \ Vm^{-1}$ in the polythene
7. $V = 50 \ kV$
8. For a 1 mm slab of mica and an airgap of 0.1 mm
   $V = 801 \ V$.
9. The effect of the tank walls on the electrostatic field is so slight that we can consider the polythene-covered sphere as an isolated sphere in an infinite sea of oil.
   We can then write:

$$V = -\int_{5 \ cm}^{7 \ cm} \frac{Q}{4\pi\varepsilon_0\varepsilon_1 r^2} \, dr - \int_{7 \ cm}^{\infty} \frac{Q}{4\pi\varepsilon_0\varepsilon_2 r^2} \, dr$$

from which,

$$\frac{Q}{4\pi\varepsilon_0} = -21 \ 10^3$$

$$E \text{ in oil} = \frac{Q}{4\pi\varepsilon_0\varepsilon_2 r^2}$$

and the maximum value is

$$-21\ 10^3 \cdot \frac{10^4}{2.049} = -2.12\ 10^6\ \text{Vm}^{-1}$$

$$E \text{ in polythene} = \frac{Q}{4\pi\varepsilon_0\varepsilon_1 r^2}$$

and the maximum value is $-3.5\ 10^6\ \text{Vm}^{-1}$.
(What is the significance of the negative sign?)

10. (i) At constant voltage, E remains at 50 kVm^{-1}
    (ii) $Q = \varepsilon_0\varepsilon_r E\ A = 4.4\ 10^{-9}$ C

    (iii) $\dfrac{Q-Q_1}{Q} = \dfrac{1}{\varepsilon_r}\ \ Q_1 = Q\left[1-\dfrac{1}{\varepsilon_r}\right] = 0.75\ Q = 3.3\ 10^{-9}$ C

    (iv) $E_i = \dfrac{Q_1}{\varepsilon_0 A} = 150$ kVm^{-1}

    or $E_i = E_0\left[1-\dfrac{1}{\varepsilon_r}\right] = 0.75\ E_0 = 0.75$

    $\varepsilon_r E_r = 150$ kVm^{-1}

11. Referring to figure T5.7 we can write the potential

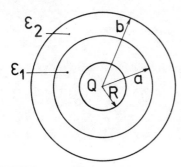

Fig. T5.7

of the foil with respect to the earth as

$$V_f = -\int_b^a E_2\ \text{d}r$$

where E_2 is the electric field strength at radius r for $a < r < b$. Using Gauss' law and assuming a long straight cylindrical conductor with negligible end effects, we have an expression for E_2:

$$E_2 = \frac{(Q-Q_2)}{2\pi r L\varepsilon_0} = \frac{Q}{2\pi r L\varepsilon_0} \cdot \frac{(Q-Q_2)}{Q} = \frac{Q}{2\pi r L\varepsilon_0\varepsilon_2}$$

(remember that we use the resultant charge inside the Gaussian surface).

These two equations give us V_f in terms of Q and L which we do not know. But, we do know the

potential of the inner conductor with respect to earth, and we can then write,

$$V = -\int_b^a E_2\ \text{d}r - \int_a^R E_1\ \text{d}r,$$

where E_1 is the electric field strength at radius r for $R < r < a$,

$$V = -\int_b^a \frac{Q}{2\pi r L\varepsilon_0\varepsilon_2}\ \text{d}r - \int_a^R \frac{Q}{2\pi r L\varepsilon_0\varepsilon_1}\ \text{d}r$$

$$= \frac{Q}{2\pi\varepsilon_0 L}\left[-\frac{\ln a/b}{\varepsilon_2} - \frac{\ln R/a}{\varepsilon_1}\right]$$

so that

$$\frac{Q}{2\pi\varepsilon_0 L} = 180{,}000$$

$$\therefore V_f = -\frac{Q}{2\pi\varepsilon_0 L}\int_b^a \frac{1}{\varepsilon_2 r}\ \text{d}r = 28\ \text{kV}$$

This means that we have 52 kV across the inner cylinder of paper and it does make one wonder if this is a proper use of expensive materials. If all the paper is designed to withstand the same high breakdown stress then the paper in the outer cylinder is being run much below its rated capability. Perhaps we should also ask whether this difference in potentials is significantly affected by the difference in relative permittivities or whether it is mainly a function of the geometry. Why not run through the solution again assuming that all the paper has the same permittivity?

And finally the solution to our student's problem. Where he made his mistake was in overlooking the effect which is illustrated in equation T5.1. By introducing a slab of Nylon he reduced the electric field strength in the space occupied by the Nylon by a factor of ε_r. If the total voltage across the capacitor was to remain unchanged it followed that the electric field strength in the remaining air space would have to increase. Since the field strength in the airgap was at 2.8 MV m^{-1} before introducing the Nylon it was very likely that it would increase above the critical value of 3 MV m^{-1}. This is in fact what happened. The final calculated value for E in the airgap was found to be 4.35 10^6 Vm^{-1}. Check for yourself.

CHAPTER 11

Tracking, treeing and bushings

11.1 INTRODUCTION

Every electrical engineer accepts the need for electrical insulation, but not everyone appreciates that the choice of electrical insulation can modify substantially the overall design and performance of electrical equipment. Like most engineering decisions, the choice has to be a compromise. The insulation may have as its main function the electrical isolation of conductors, but in many cases it will also have to act as a mechanical support or reinforcement. If it is gaseous or liquid it may be used as a coolant and if it is solid one has to be sure that it will not become so hot in use that it causes a fire. Finding the right insulation to meet all the requirements is not easy, but the rewards for success are substantial. There are examples of electrical equipment being up-rated by 50 per cent in the same frame size as a result of the introduction of new materials. We might therefore ask why it is that much electrical insulation is worked at stresses well below the breakdown stress. Polythene, for example, has a breakdown strength of 8 MV cm^{-1} measured under laboratory conditions, but in practice it is usually worked at stresses in the region of 0.2 MV cm^{-1}. The reason for this very large factor of safety is partly that the material has to withstand mechanical stresses which may require a thickness in excess of the electrical requirement, but the material may also have to withstand the effects of electrical discharges which can begin at comparatively low values of average electrical stress. These discharges may occur across the insulation surface, within the body of the insulation or in the surrounding space. Discharges across the surface can give rise to surface damage, as shown in figure 11.1, and this is known as tracking.

11.2 TRACKING

To explain this phenomenon let us consider a flat sheet of insulation exposed to the weather. We connect a high-voltage source to electrodes positioned at the top and bottom of the sheet and under clean, dry conditions we would expect a negligible flow of current

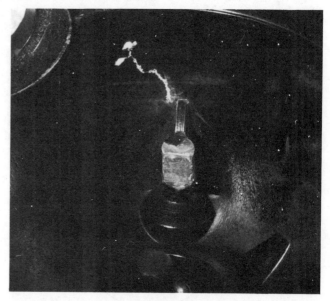

Fig. 11.1

through the insulation and indeed across the surface. But, if the surface becomes dirty and damp we will find that a leakage current will flow across the surface within the slightly conducting film of moist pollution. The current flow produces heat in the polluted layer which will tend to dry it out. Obviously the whole surface will not dry out at the same rate and we will be left with a patchwork of wet and dry bands. As more moisture falls on the surface, the dry areas become proportionally smaller and smaller until a time is reached when there is almost a continuous path of moisture between the electrodes with only one small break across a dry band. We then have a condition in which all the potential difference appears across the small dry band and, if other conditions are right, there is an electrical discharge across the band through the air. If the insulation is organic the spark will carbonise the surface and a permanent conducting track is formed. Subsequent discharges will increase the length of the track until it completely bridges the insulating sheet. This shorts out the electrodes and the insulation is irreparably damaged. Certain precautions can be taken to protect insulation which may be exposed to dust and damp. It has been common practice in the past to grease the surface of insulators on high-voltage lines. Particles of pollution are absorbed and insulated by the grease film and surface moisture forms beads and not a continuous film. This alleviates the problem but the method does have some obvious disadvantages. An alternative is to apply a semiconducting layer to the surface. This controls the potential gradient across the surface and prevents the stress across the dry band from becoming excessive. Many overhead-line, ceramic insulators are coated with a semiconducting glaze and semiconducting varnishes may be used on the end-windings of high-voltage machines.

Where the insulation does not carbonise and track, there can still be damage due to erosion by the spark; although this is more common when the discharge occurs as a result of the breakdown of an adjacent material. In the last Task we met a problem which arose from the insertion of a Nylon slab in an airgap. The subsequent discharge in the air would, over a period of time, damage the Nylon and perhaps lead to total breakdown. The effect is often seen at edges and discontinuities. A classic case occurs when a sphere at high potential rests on a slab of insulation (figure 11.2).

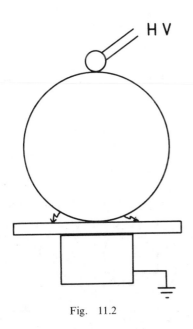

Fig. 11.2

Discharges in the air space between the sphere and the insulation are almost inevitable.

Much of the damage to the insulation is initially caused by particle bombardment, although chemical effects can be significant. To start with, particle bombardment will gradually and uniformly erode away the insulation surface, but with time the erosion becomes centred in small pits and from these pits discharge

channels will propagate into the insulation forming trees.

11.3 TREEING

This can best be described in terms of a straightforward laboratory experiment. Imagine a slab of clear Perspex, 1 cm thick, with a very sharply pointed needle pressed into one of the large flat surfaces to a depth of about 0.5 cm. A large, flat conducting electrode is pressed against the opposite face to give the kind of arrangement illustrated in figure 11.3. The slab is placed in a light-proof box and viewed at a distance through a telescope.

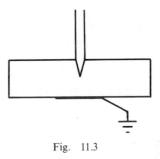

Fig. 11.3

A series of voltage impulses is then applied between the needle and the plane electrode.

If the first impulse has a magnitude of about 120 kV and each successive impulse is increased by 10 per cent

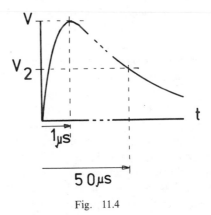

Fig. 11.4

then a time will come when the observer will see a small flash of light within the slab of Perspex. If the Perspex is then removed and examined, a small hollow channel will be seen extending from the tip of the needle into the body of the slab. Continued repetition of the experiment will result in the development of a branching network of these small channels giving rise to the kind of channel pattern illustrated in figure 11.5.

Despite this 'treeing' effect, the slab of insulation will still behave electrically as if it were as good as new. We

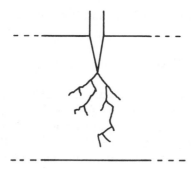

Fig. 11.5

only know that damage has taken place because we can see it. One can appreciate therefore the difficulties faced by an engineer in assessing the more normal type of opaque insulation.

An early study of treeing in polythene-insulated cables illustrated the point well. The investigators took out of service an apparently healthy length of cable and carefully pared away the insulation to reveal a number of trees in various stages of development. In this case, of course, the cable was a normal a.c. cable and had not been subjected to periodic voltage impulses. It is clear then that this treeing phenomenon can occur under normal operation.

At its most simple we can explain the production of a discharge channel as the result of an electron avalanche in the material. Taking the case of a negative point we can visualise an electron avalanche moving into the material and fading away as it moves into a weaker and weaker field. It leaves a positive space charge behind it and this propagates back to the point creating a region of ionised dielectric along the track of the original avalanche. This ionised region vaporises and leaves behind a small hollow channel. The real phenomenon is exceedingly complex because it is affected by changes in the field pattern, by chemical reaction due to the discharge products, by the nature of the material being used and by thermal effects.

The way it has been described here, we would expect treeing to occur from sharp points within insulation. This is correct, but it can also occur as a result of discharges impinging on the dielectric surface. These discharges may start outside the dielectric, as in figure 11.2, or they may start within voids, or bubbles, within the dielectric itself. Because of this, rigid control is exercised over the manufacture of polymeric and resin-based insulation to keep voids down to a minimum and paper-based impregnated insulation is carefully vacuum dried before impregnation so that any voids that may form in service will fill with impregnant and not with air or water vapour.

11.4 BUSHINGS

Let us start with a problem. How do we take a high-voltage conductor through the tank wall of a transformer or a switch? We clearly need insulation and in this case we cannot use air because we would then have a gaping hole in the side of our apparatus. So we select a solid insulator which gives mechanical support as well as electrical isolation. Figure 11.6 shows a section through a possible arrangement of conductor and insulator. The insulator in this case would be a straight cylinder and we would describe it as a bushing.

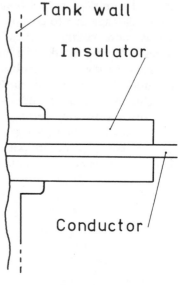

Fig. 11.6

Let us now roughly plot the pattern of the electrostatic field around the conductor, assuming the tank wall is at earth potential. Figure 11.7 illustrates some of

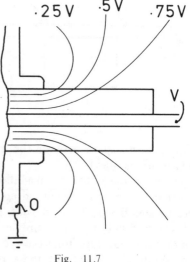

Fig. 11.7

the equipotential lines. We need to recall that the electric force vectors cross these lines at right angles and that the closer these lines are the greater is the electric field strength. The high electric field strength in the solid insulation is of no real concern to us at the moment because we shall assume that the insulation was chosen to withstand such a stress, but the field pattern on the surface of the insulator is of considerable interest. Note first of all that the electric force has a component acting along the surface, and then note how this force is greatest close to the earthed tank wall. It is possible that a surface discharge may occur in the region close to the tank under clean dry conditions, but it is very likely that a discharge will occur if the surface is dirty and damp. To reduce the probability we must modify the electrostatic field so as to reduce the high stress region along the insulator surface. This is achieved by inserting in the bushing a series of concentric cylinders made of thin conducting foil. There is no direct connection made to them. They assume a potential with respect to earth which is determined by the capacitances of the system. For the sake of simplicity we assume that

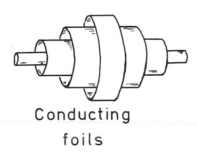

Conducting
foils

Fig. 11.8

the foils shown in figure 11.8 adopt potentials of 0.25 V, 0.5 V and 0.75 V.

The modified field pattern in and around the new bushing is shown in figure 11.9. By comparison with figure 11.7 we can see that the electric field strength along the insulator surface near the tank is reduced.

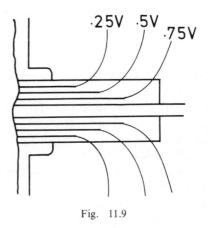

Fig. 11.9

Next time you are near a high-voltage sub-station have a look at how the bare, overhead lines are brought down to transformers, switches and cable ends. In each case there is a bushing and they will all have some form of electrostatic stress control designed into them.

FURTHER READING

High Voltage Technology, L. L. Alston, Oxford University Press, 1968.

CHAPTER 12

Task 6: Capacitance

T6.1 INTRODUCTION

We have learned from Tasks 2 and 3 that a charged electrostatic system has potential energy. It can be thought of as an energy store. The energy has to come from the electrical source and if the source is an electrical signal passing along a line then energy will be taken from the signal. We can make use of this effect in controlling and modifying electrical signals.

The capacity of a system or device to store energy in its electric field can be defined in terms of its capacitance and capacitance is, as you well know, an important circuit parameter. One perplexing feature of capacitance is that you cannot get away from it. It is always there, to some extent, and although in some applications we can ignore it on the grounds that the effect is insignificant we can never forget it because a change in frequency, or even temperature, may bring it back into prominence. We must therefore be able to calculate or measure capacitance so that we can take account of the undesirable effects as well as being able to introduce extra capacitance for our own purposes.

T6.2 OBJECTIVES

When you have finished this Task you should be able to do the following:

(a) define capacitance in terms of charge and electric potential;
(b) calculate the capacitances of the following geometric arrangements—
  (i) a parallel-plate capacitor
  (ii) a concentric, cylindrical cable
  (iii) a straight, twin-conductor line; and
(c) calculate the total capacitance of several capacitors connected in series or parallel.

T6.3 PRIOR KNOWLEDGE

It is important that you should have worked through the previous Tasks. It will be assumed here that you are familiar with the methods used for determining potential difference and electric field strength in and around the geometries of charged conductors mentioned above.

T6.4 CAPACITANCE OF A PARALLEL-PLATE SYSTEM

We have shown in Tasks 2 and 3 that electric potential is directly proportional to charge. We can therefore write:

$$Q = CV$$

where C is constant for a given system. C is defined as the capacitance of the system. The unit of capacitance is the FARAD. This is a very large quantity and in most applications we find capacitance values lie in the following range:

microfarads, $\mu F = 10^{-6}$ farad, and
picofarads, $pF = 10^{-12}$ farad.

The parallel-plate capacitor is a convenient system with which to demonstrate the calculation of capacitance. The system consists simply of two parallel, conducting plates, each of area A, separated by a distance d. We assume a charge of magnitude Q on each plate, a potential difference V and free space between the plates.

Before rushing into a proof, let us consider what it is we are trying to do so that we can plan out a solution. Essentially, we need the ratio of Q to V. This means obtaining an expression for V written in terms of Q—a simple cross multiplication then gives C. So how do we connect V and Q? There is a common factor—the electric field strength. The connection between V and E was covered in Task 3 and the one between Q and E in Task 4.

Using the sign conventions of Task 3 for the case illustrated in figure T6.1, we have:

$$V_{AB} = -\int_B^A E\, dx = -\int_d^0 E\, dx$$

E in terms of Q can be obtained by applying Gauss' law, or we can say that the flux density at the surface of the

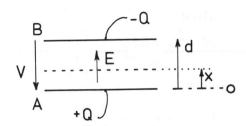

Fig. T6.1

plates is:

$$D = \frac{Q}{A}$$

and, assuming a uniform field, D is the same at all points between the plates.
Now,

$$\varepsilon_0 E = D$$

so that

$$\varepsilon_0 E = \frac{Q}{A}$$

hence

$$V_{AB} = -\int_d^0 \frac{Q}{\varepsilon_0 A} \cdot dx = \frac{Q}{\varepsilon_0 A} \cdot d$$

and it follows that

$$C = \frac{Q}{V_{AB}} = \frac{\varepsilon_0 A}{d} \qquad \text{(T6.1)}$$

If the space between the plates is filled with a dielectric of relative permittivity ε_r then the above equation is modified as follows:

$$C = \frac{\varepsilon_0 \varepsilon_r A}{d} \qquad \text{(T6.2)}$$

We can see from this that we could use the measured ratio of these two capacitances to determine ε_r.

Question 1

The capacitance of a parallel-plate electrode system is 10 pF in vacuum. Calculate the capacitance of the system when the space between the electrodes is filled with:
(a) glass, of relative permittivity 6, and
(b) de-ionised water of relative permittivity 80.

Question 2

Would either of the above systems make usable capacitors?

T6.5 CAPACITANCE BETWEEN TWO LONG, STRAIGHT, PARALLEL CONDUCTORS

Figure T6.2 represents a section through two such conductors with dimensions defined. The procedure to be followed is the same as in section T6.4 but with different equations because of the different geometries.

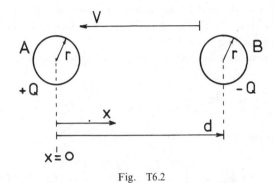

Fig. T6.2

There is also a danger here of confusion over the signs allocated to different quantities and it is worth taking trouble to get these correct. Recall that in Task 3 we defined E acting positively along a line of increasing x. We then defined the potential of a point at $x = A$ with respect to a point at $x = B$ as

$$V_{AB} = -\int_B^A E \, dx$$

At a point a general distance x away from the axis of conductor A, as defined in figure T6.3, the electric field strength has two components; one due to the charge on A and one due to the charge on B. We assume that $Q_A = -Q_B = Q$, so that the total charge on the system is zero. (If this were not so we would have to assume the presence of a third charged body.)

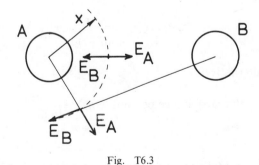

Fig. T6.3

Theoretically, it does not matter which path we take when we determine the potential difference between two points, but for ease of calculation we choose the one that gives the easiest solution. In this case the choice is the shortest line between the two axes. At the point x

along this line the two components of E are:

$$E \text{ at } x \text{ due to charge on } A = \frac{Q}{2\pi\varepsilon_0 xL} \qquad (T6.3)$$

and

$$E \text{ at } x \text{ due to charge on } B = \frac{-Q}{2\pi\varepsilon_0 (d-x)L} \qquad (T6.4)$$

The field defined by equation T6.3 acts along the line from A to B. The field defined by equation T6.4 acts along the line from B to A.

The resultant field at x acting from A to B is therefore

$$E_R = \frac{Q}{2\pi\varepsilon_0 xL} - \left[\frac{-Q}{2\pi\varepsilon_0 (d-x)L} \right]$$

It follows that

$$V_{AB} = -\int_{d-r}^{r} \frac{Q}{2\pi\varepsilon_0 L} \left[\frac{1}{x} + \frac{1}{(d-x)} \right] dx \qquad (T6.5)$$

Note the limits of integration. The potential difference exists between the surfaces of the conductors i.e. $x = r$ and $x = d - r$.

Now,

$$\int_{d-r}^{r} \frac{1}{x} dx = \left[\ln x \right]_{d-r}^{r} = \ln\left(\frac{r}{d-r} \right)$$

and

$$\int_{d-r}^{r} \frac{dx}{(d-x)} = \left[-\ln (d-x) \right]_{d-r}^{r} = \ln\left(\frac{r}{d-r} \right)$$

therefore

$$V_{AB} = \frac{Q}{\pi\varepsilon_0 L} \ln\left(\frac{d-r}{r} \right)$$

so that

$$C = \frac{Q}{V_{AB}} = \frac{\pi\varepsilon_0 L}{\ln (d-r)/r} \qquad (T6.6)$$

or alternatively

$$\text{the capacitance per unit length} = \frac{\pi\varepsilon_0}{\ln (d-r)/r}$$

T6.6 CAPACITANCE OF A COAXIAL CABLE

A section through such a cable is represented by figure T6.4. The electrostatic field will have a cylindrical geometry and the equations we develop will be similar to the ones for the two parallel conductors. However, there is an important difference and that is in the equation

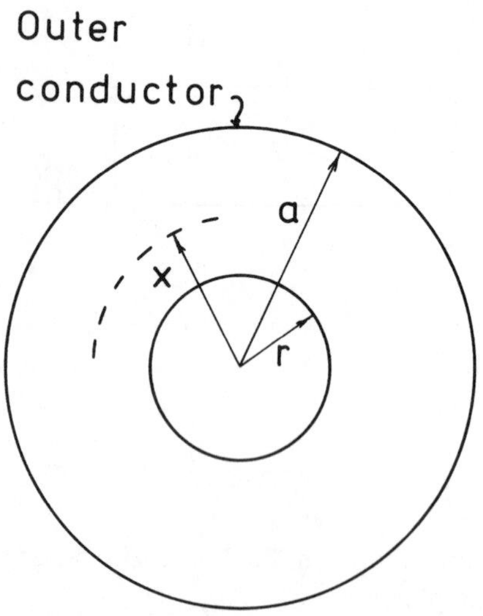

Outer conductor

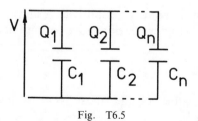

Fig. T6.4

for the electric field strength at a general radius x for $r < x < a$. If in doubt refer back to the work on Gauss' law.

Question 3

Derive an expression for the capaciance per unit length of the coaxial cable represented in figure T6.4. Assume that the space between the conductors is filled with air of permittivity ε_0.

T6.7 CAPACITORS IN PARALLEL

Figure T6.5 represents several capacitors connected in parallel and we can observe that the potential difference across each capacitor is the same. If this were not so, charge would flow along the interconnecting wires until the potentials were the same.

Thus

$$V_1 = V_2 = V_3 = \ldots = V_n = V$$

Each capacitor carries a charge and the total charge carried by the system will be the sum of the individual charges,

$$Q_T = Q_1 + Q_2 + Q_3 + \ldots + Q_n$$

Fig. T6.5

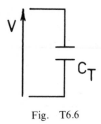

Fig. T6.6

or

$$Q_T = VC_1 + VC_2 + VC_3 + \ldots + VC_n$$

$$\frac{Q_T}{V} = C_1 + C_2 + C_3 + \ldots + C_n$$

So that the effect of all the capacitors is the same as the effect of one resultant capacitor of value C_T, having a total charge Q_T and a potential difference across it of V, for which

$$C_T = \frac{Q_T}{V}$$

Thus figures T6.5 and T6.6 can be considered equivalent provided that:

$$C_T = C_1 + C_2 + \ldots + C_n$$

T6.8 CAPACITORS IN SERIES

If we place a charge $+Q$ on plate a on figure T6.7 then there will be a flow of charge $+Q$ from the opposite plate, b. This appears on plate c as a charge $+Q$ leaving a deficiency of charge $-Q$ on plate b. The process continues until the last plate in the line shows a deficit of $-Q$. The magnitude of the charge on each capacitor has to be the same. Thus:

$$Q_1 = Q_2 = Q_3 \ldots = Q_n = Q$$

The total potential difference V across all the capacitors is:

$$V = V_1 + V_2 + V_3 + \ldots + V_n$$

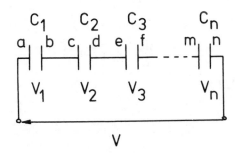

Fig. T6.7

or

$$V = \frac{Q}{C_1} + \frac{Q}{C_2} + \frac{Q}{C_3} + \ldots + \frac{Q}{C_n}$$

giving

$$V = Q\left(\frac{1}{C_1} + \frac{1}{C_2} + \frac{1}{C_3} + \ldots + \frac{1}{C_n}\right)$$

Thus the system may be considered equivalent to one capacitor, having a potential difference V, carrying a charge Q and having a capacitance C_T, given by

$$\frac{1}{C_T} = \frac{1}{C_1} + \frac{1}{C_2} + \frac{1}{C_3} + \ldots + \frac{1}{C_n}$$

T6.9 SELF-ASSESSMENT QUESTIONS

Question 4

A parallel-plate capacitor consists of two plates, each in the form of a disc of diameter 10 cm. They are positioned 0.25 cm apart in transformer oil of relative permittivity 2.3. Calculate the capacitance between the plates.

Question 5

Two concentric conducting cylinders of diameters 0.6 m and 0.2 m form an air-spaced coaxial line. Determine the capacitance per metre length.

Question 6

Two long, straight, cylindrical conductors run in parallel to form a 'go and return' electric circuit. Each conductor has an outside diameter of 2 cm and they are separated by a distance of 1 m between centres. Determine the capacitance between the conductors per metre run.

Question 7

A parallel-plate capacitor with two dielectrics is illustrated in figure T6.8. The total area of each plate is 0.7 m^2, the separation of the plates is 0.4 cm and the relative permittivities of the two dielectrics are 2.3 and 3.8. Calculate the capacitance.

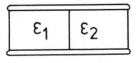

Fig. T6.8

Question 8

A concentric cable consists of an inner conductor of diameter 2 cm and an outer conductor of internal diameter 6 cm. Polythene tape is wrapped around the inner conductor to a thickness of 1 cm, and then a layer of Nylon tape is laid on top of the polythene to fill completely the space between the two conductors.

Calculate the capacitance of the cable per metre run. Take ε_r for polythene as 2.4 and ε_r for Nylon as 3.6.

Question 9

A hollow conducting sphere of 4 m diameter is placed in a large laboratory so that it is remote from other conducting surfaces. Estimate the capacitance of the sphere to earth.

T6.10 ANSWERS AND SOLUTIONS

1. (a) 60 pF   (b) 800 pF

2. This question was put in to emphasise again the point that engineering decisions are complex and involve many variables. One cannot choose a capacitor on its capacitance value alone. We need to know the voltage it has to withstand, or the current it must pass, and frequency is important. A capacitor which is acceptable for d.c. operation might have significant losses at 10^6 Hz which could lead to overheating and fire. Glass capacitors are usually found within the range 10^{-12} to 10^{-9} F. Water filled capacitors are never used, although special applications may be found in which conducting plates are separated in a water ambient. The problem here is that the water has a relatively low resistivity; for de-ionised water a figure of 10^6 Ω cm would be reasonable, so that it is useless as a dielectric for d.c. or a.c. operation.

3. Let us assume a positive charge Q on the inner conductor so that the electric field strength E acts radially outwards from the centre in the direction of increasing x. We define the potential of the inner conductor with respect to the outer as:

$$V = -\int_a^r E \, dx$$

and we note that E varies with x. Applying Gauss' law

to an equipotential surface of radius x gives:

$$E \text{ at } x = \frac{Q}{2\pi\varepsilon_0 x L}$$

So that

$$V = -\int_a^r \frac{Q \, dx}{2\pi\varepsilon_0 x L} = \frac{Q}{2\pi\varepsilon_0 L} \cdot \ln(a/r)$$

giving

$$C = \frac{2\pi\varepsilon_0}{\ln(a/r)} \text{ farads per metre length}$$

4. $C = 27.8$ pF

5. $C = 50.6$ pF m^{-1}

6. $C = 6.04$ pF m^{-1}

7. $C = 4720$ pF

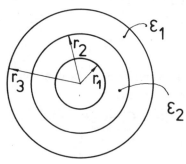

Fig. T6.9

8. Applying the argument of solution 3 to the case illustrated in figure T6.9.

$$V = -\int_{r_3}^{r_2} E_1 \, dx - \int_{r_2}^{r_1} E_2 \, dx$$

$$E_1 \text{ at } x \text{ for } r_2 < x < r_3 = \frac{Q}{2\pi\varepsilon_0\varepsilon_1 x L}$$

$$E_2 \text{ at } x \text{ for } r_1 < x < r_2 = \frac{Q}{2\pi\varepsilon_0\varepsilon_2 x L}$$

so that

$$V = \frac{Q}{2\pi\varepsilon_0 L}\left(\frac{1}{\varepsilon_1}\ln\frac{r_3}{r_2} + \frac{1}{\varepsilon_2}\ln\frac{r_2}{r_1}\right)$$

Hence

$$C = \frac{Q}{VL} = 140 \text{ pF m}^{-1}$$

9. $C = 222$ pF

CHAPTER 13

Charge-coupled devices

13.1 INTRODUCTION

Announced in 1970, the charge-coupled device (c.c.d.) promises to have as great an impact on our lives as did the transistor. It is a semiconductor device based on a silicon chip and fabricated by techniques which are well established and understood. It differs from the transistor in its mode of operation. The transistor modifies electric currents, the c.c.d. manipulates information which is carried in the form of discrete packets of charge. A silicon chip which could hold between three and four thousand computer-memory elements with transistor technology can hold four times the amount using c.c.d. techniques.

Whether or not the c.c.d. can be described as an electrostatic device is a question for debate. It is introduced here for two reasons. Firstly, as we consider the operation of the device we begin to see how arbitrary are the divisions between subjects. When does 'electronics' become 'electrical science' or 'field theory'? And if we extend the idea, when is 'field theory' 'circuit theory' and when do both become 'electrical machines'? Secondly, we can again appreciate that a knowledge of the basic concepts and principles of electrical engineering enables us to understand the principles of a wide variety of devices.

13.2 THE POTENTIAL WELL

If we move an electron away from a positively charged plate we do work against the force of attraction between the charges and as a result we increase the potential energy of the electron. If we release the electron it will return to the plate. Figure 13.1 shows how the potential energy of an electron might vary as it occupied various positions from A, past a positively charged plate at B and on to C. The electron would clearly prefer to be at B, which is a position of minimum potential energy. What is true for a line through ABC is also true for any straight line through B. Thus any free electron in the region will tend to move towards B. In the jargon of semiconductor physics, B is a 'potential well' into

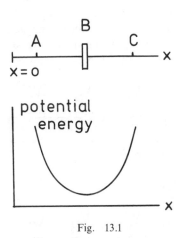

Fig. 13.1

which electrons fall and like any well it can be filled up, in this case with electronic charge.

A positively charged plate on the surface of a slab of material will produce a potential well in the material immediately below the plate. This is the principle used to hold charge in a c.c.d. The c.c.d. is represented in figure 13.2. The surface of a wafer of p-type silicon is oxidised and a series of conducting electrodes are laid on top of the oxide layer. If one electrode is made positive, by about 10 V, a potential well is formed beneath it. The insulating layer prevents any movement of charge from the electrode into the bulk of the silicon and any packet of charge in the potential well will be held there until the potentials of the electrodes change.

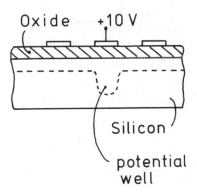

Fig. 13.2

13.3 CHARGE TRANSFER

Figure 13.3 shows a series of situations which occur as adjacent electrodes are pulsed with the voltage waveforms shown. In the original position a packet of charge is trapped in the first potential well. As the adjacent electrode is made positive the charge spreads itself under the two electrodes. Finally, the potential on the first electrode is reduced causing the electrons underneath it to move into the adjacent potential well.

A series of regular voltage pulses applied to the row of electrodes will cause the packet of charge to propagate just below the surface of the insulating layer from one side of the device to the other. This can be done using a

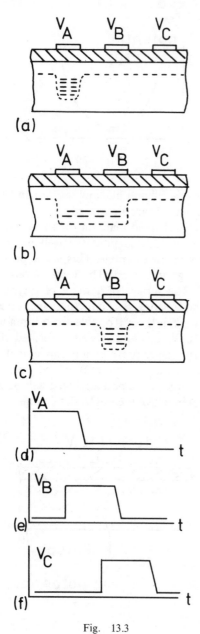

Fig. 13.3

three-phase clocking system as illustrated in figure 13.4. Note how the voltage pulses have relatively slow falling edges. This is to avoid driving the electronic charge into the silicon substrate. The slowness of the falling edge allows the electronic charge sufficient time to move into the adjacent well. The speed of transfer depends on the magnitude of the forces acting on the electron. As an adjacent well is opened the electrons spread rapidly as a result of the forces of repulsion between like charges. The movement is aided by the forces due to the electric field produced by the electrodes. As the previous well is closed, with the decrease in potential of the associated electrode, the field-induced forces predominate and move the remainder of the charge into the new position. As one might expect, it is easier to move the first portion than the last and the final portion, perhaps 5 per cent, of the packet tends to move by diffusion rather than by field forcing. This is a relatively slow process, and perhaps more than anything else puts the upper limit on the operating frequency of these devices. Even so the c.c.d. will operate at clock rates of 10^7 Hz.

13.4 INPUT AND OUTPUT

The earliest devices used an input diode which was fabricated on the same chip as the c.c.d. The input diffusion in figure 13.5 provides the charge source and a

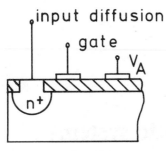

input diffusion

gate

V_A

n⁺

Fig. 13.5

positive pulse applied to the input gate will allow charge to pass through into the first well if that well is 'open'. Obviously the pulse on the input gate needs to be synchronised with the pulse on the first c.c.d. electrode.

The output from the c.c.d. is via an on-chip amplifier. Again there is a control, or output, gate which operates in synchronism with the final electrode to allow the charge packets to pass through into the output amplifier.

If we now think back to the section on the electrostatic copier we will recall that silicon was used as the imaging material because it was photoconductive. Light falling on to silicon is partially absorbed and a quantity of electronic charge is generated in the material. The amount of charge produced is proportional to the intensity of the light, so that it is possible to put the charge into a c.c.d. by optical means and have a stored quantity proportional to the input signal. This opens up a range of interesting uses for the c.c.d. because it is now possible to envisage inputs to the device occurring at various sites on the surface at the same instant.

13.5 IMAGING APPLICATIONS

The simplest form of this is the linear sensor illustrated in figure 13.6. A row of photo-sensors is exposed to the light from a strip of the optical image being processed. Sufficient time is allowed for the charge in the photo-sensor to build up and then the input gates are switched to transfer the charge into the row of elements forming the c.c.d. A clocking pulse now moves the charge packets to the right where they are read out as a video signal. Whilst this is happening, the photo-sensors are being exposed to the next strip of the optical image. As the process continues a complete video signal is built up of the whole image. This system requires that either the image or the photo-sensors move to give complete coverage of the picture.

A more advanced method of imaging uses area sensors. In this case the sensors are arranged in an M × N flat matrix and the whole image is exposed at one instant. The M × N packets of charge are then switched into a series of stores and each row in the store is read out in turn while a second view of the image is taken by the photo-sensor array. One obvious application of this is in television camera technology. The c.c.d. is a low-voltage, low-power device and this gives a clear advantage, but even more important is the fact that the location of each photo-sensor in an array is known exactly and this can lead to much better alignment in colour cameras. It is also an important feature where image magnification is required, as in photo-reconnaisance.

FURTHER READING

Charge-Coupled Devices, J. D. E. Beynon, *Radio & Electronic Engineer*, Vol. 45, No. 11, pp. 647–656, Nov. 1975.

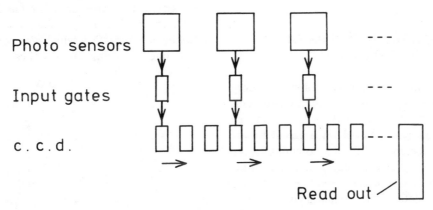

Photo sensors

Input gates

c.c.d.

Read out

Fig. 13.6

CHAPTER 14

Task 7 : Energy in electrostatic systems

T7.1 INTRODUCTION

One important reason for wanting to know about energy storage is that we can determine the forces acting in an electrostatic system from a consideration of energy change in the system. The method used is in fact applicable to the electromagnetic case as well. What we shall do in this Task is to develop equations which describe energy storage in electrostatic systems. We shall then use these equations to develop the technique for calculating force.

T7.2 OBJECTIVES

When you have finished this Task you should be able to do the following:

(a) define energy stored in an electrostatic system in terms of potential and capacitance;

(b) define energy stored in an electrostatic system in terms of the field quantities E and D;

(c) apply the principle of virtual work in the determination of the force between the plates of a charged, parallel-plate capacitor; and

(d) determine the forces in an electrostatic system from a knowledge of the energy change in the system.

T7.3 ENERGY STORED IN TERMS OF CAPACITANCE AND POTENTIAL

A charged electrostatic system has potential energy which can be released by discharging the system. This can be demonstrated by short-circuiting a charged capacitor. Let us base our model on a parallel-plate capacitor which can be charged from a potential source which rises from zero to a final value V in a finite time. As the charging process proceeds, negative charge will accumulate on one plate of the capacitor and positive charge on the other. At some instant in time we will have a potential difference between the plates, v, and a charge on the plates, q.

52

To move the next increment of charge δq from one plate to the other requires an amount of work δW.

$$\delta W = v \delta q$$

To build up a total charge Q across a final potential V requires a total work done W, where

$$W = \int_0^Q v \, \mathrm{d}q$$

and from the known relationship between v, q and C

$$W = \int_0^Q \frac{q}{C} \, \mathrm{d}q = \frac{Q^2}{2C}$$

Since, in the final state $Q = CV$, this equation can be written as

$$W = \frac{1}{2}\frac{Q^2}{C} = \frac{1}{2}QV = \frac{1}{2}CV^2 \qquad \text{(T7.1)}$$

This work is done charging up the capacitor and it is stored in the capacitor as potential energy.

T7.4 ENERGY STORED IN TERMS OF THE FIELD QUANTITIES E AND D

It is sometimes easier to think of energy being stored in the electrostatic field rather than in the capacitance. We arrive at the same answer by using a different model.

Consider the thin tube, shown in figure T7.1, of cross-section δA and sides which are parallel to the electric flow lines. No flux crosses these sides and therefore,

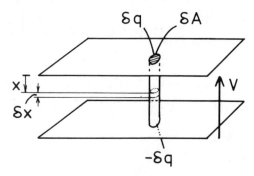

Fig. T7.1

within the tube

$$D = \frac{\delta q}{\delta A} \text{ or } \delta q = D\delta A$$

The potential difference along the tube is

$$V = -\sum_{d}^{0} E\,\delta x$$

The energy stored in the tube is

$$\delta W = \frac{1}{2} V\delta q = -\frac{1}{2}\sum_{d}^{0} DE\,\delta A\delta x$$

Over the capacitor as a whole, the energy stored is:

$$W = -\frac{1}{2}\sum_{Ad}^{0} DE\,\delta\text{vol} = -\frac{1}{2}\int_{Ad}^{0} DE\,\text{dvol} \quad \text{(T7.2)}$$

where δvol represents the small volume $\delta A\delta x$
Thus

$$W = \frac{1}{2} DEAd \quad \text{(T7.3)}$$

Equation T7.3 is true for a parallel-plate capacitor and you can show that it is equal to equation T7.1. The more important equation is T7.2 because this applies to any field geometry. Provided that the small volume that we are referring to has sides that run parallel to the flow lines we can say that the energy stored in the small volume is given by equation T7.2. Figure T7.2 shows a general case.

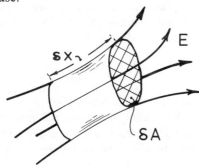

Fig. T7.2

T7.5 THE DETERMINATION OF FORCES IN THE ELECTROSTATIC FIELD

There are two distinct cases which we may consider. The first is an electrostatic system under conditions of constant charge, i.e. no charge transfer into or out of the system is possible. The second is an electrostatic system under conditions of constant potential. In this case charge can be transferred to or from the source of constant potential.

T7.5.1 System Maintained at Constant Charge

The method we adopt for calculating force is based on the principle of virtual work. We start off with the system in static equilibrium and we then imagine that the electric forces move the charged body, or part of the charged system, through an infinitesimal distance δx. We assume that the displacement δx is so small that there is no observable change in the forces within the system.

In figure T7.3 x is defined as increasing positively along the line of action of the electric field strength.

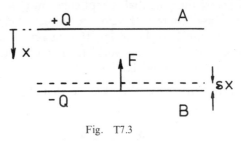

Fig. T7.3

From our previous work we would expect the plates to be drawn together by the action of the charges, so let us define F in figure T7.3 as the force between the plates. Note that F acts in the direction of negative x. Now consider plate A fixed and B free to move through a small distance of magnitude δx. The work done by the system as F acts through $-\delta x$ is

$$\delta W = -F\delta x$$

No energy loss occurs and therefore

Work done by the system + Change in electrical stored energy = zero
or

$$\delta W + \delta W_e = 0$$

$$\therefore\ F\delta x = \delta W_e$$

$$F = \frac{\delta W_e}{\delta x} \quad \text{(T7.4)}$$

For a parallel-plate capacitor

$$W_e = \frac{1}{2}\frac{Q^2}{C} = \frac{1}{2}\frac{Q^2 x}{\varepsilon_0 A}$$

and

$$F = \frac{dW_e}{dx} \text{ in the limit as } \delta x \to 0$$

so that

$$F = \frac{1}{2}\frac{Q^2}{\varepsilon_0 A} \quad \text{(T7.5)}$$

T7.5.2 System Maintained at Constant Potential

We shall again work in terms of the parallel-plate capacitor, but this time we note that energy can flow into the system from the potential source. Our energy balance equation now takes the form:

Work done by the system + Change in electrical stored energy = Electrical input energy

We need to examine each term of the equation and we begin with the electrical input.

Using the principle of virtual work we again allow the plates of the capacitor to move closer together by an amount δx. The capacitance will therefore increase and because the potential is kept constant $Q = CV$ must also increase. There is therefore a transfer of charge δq from the supply to the plates. If a charge δq is taken up to a potential V the work done is $V\delta q$. Thus the energy from the supply is $V\delta q$.

The energy stored is $W_e = \frac{1}{2}VQ$, so that the change in energy storage is

$$\delta W_e = \tfrac{1}{2}V\delta q$$

The work done by the force is $-F\delta x$, as before so that the energy balance equation becomes:

$$V\delta q = -F\delta x + \tfrac{1}{2}V\delta q$$

or

$$F\delta x = -\tfrac{1}{2}V\delta q = -\delta W_e$$

in the limit, as $\delta x \to 0$

$$F = -\frac{\mathrm{d}W_e}{\mathrm{d}x} \qquad \text{(T7.6)}$$

$$W_e = \frac{1}{2}CV^2 = \frac{1}{2}V^2\frac{\varepsilon_0 A}{x}$$

$$\therefore \quad -\frac{\mathrm{d}W_e}{\mathrm{d}x} = \frac{V^2}{2}\frac{\varepsilon_0 A}{x^2} = \frac{1}{2}E^2\varepsilon_0 A \qquad \text{(T7.7)}$$

You can satisfy yourself that this is the same as equation T7.5.

Let us look more closely at what is happening to energy in the constant potential case. We have decided that energy comes from the supply and that this is given by $V\delta q$. We know that energy goes into work by the action of F through a distance δx. As x decreases by an amount δx the capacitance increases so that the energy stored, $\frac{1}{2}CV^2$, increases. This energy has to come from somewhere and it comes from the supply. We thus have the situation illustrated in figure T7.4 in which the energy from the supply splits into two equal parts, one going to do work and one going into the field store.

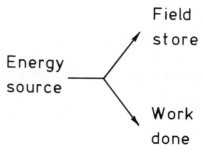

Fig. T7.4

If we reverse the process and apply an external force to do work to pull the plates apart we release an equal amount of energy from the field and the two components go to increase the energy of the supply.

In the case of constant charge, there is no transfer of energy to the supply and the energy required to do work must come from the field store.

Equation T7.6 is sometimes expanded as follows:

$$F = -\frac{\mathrm{d}W_e}{\mathrm{d}x} = -\frac{\mathrm{d}}{\mathrm{d}x}\left(\frac{1}{2}CV^2\right) = -\frac{1}{2}V^2\frac{\mathrm{d}C}{\mathrm{d}x} \qquad \text{(T7.8)}$$

We can see here a direct connection between the force and the variation of capacitance. If we do not have a variable capacitance geometry we cannot develop an electrostatic force. As an example of this consider two conducting discs forming a parallel-plate capacitor and mounted so that the discs are free to rotate about a central axis perpendicular to the plane of the discs. There is no possibility here of producing a rotational movement by electrostatic means because there is no change in capacitance with rotational position, i.e. $\mathrm{d}C/\mathrm{d}\theta$ is zero, so the torque produced, T is:

$$T = -\frac{1}{2}V^2\frac{\mathrm{d}C}{\mathrm{d}\theta} = 0$$

But, if we mount two semi-circular discs in the same way, as in figure T7.5, the application of a potential difference between them will produce a torque $T = -\frac{1}{2}V^2\,\mathrm{d}C/\mathrm{d}\theta$ which will tend to align the two halves and rotation will occur.

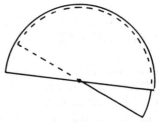

Fig. T7.5

T7.6 SELF-ASSESSMENT QUESTIONS

Question 1

A parallel-plate capacitor is charged and then isolated from the supply. The plates are then moved further apart. Describe the changes that occur in the potential difference between the plates, the energy stored in the capacitor, the electric field strength between the plates, the electric flux density and the capacitance.

Question 2

A parallel-plate capacitor is maintained at constant voltage. The plates are then moved further apart. Describe the changes that occur in the charge stored on the plates, the energy stored by the capacitor, the electric field strength between the plates, the electric flux density and the capacitance.

Question 3

An electrostatic transducer is made up of two parallel plates in air, each of area $2\,10^{-2}$ m² and separated by a distance of 5 mm. One plate is fixed and the other is free to move towards the fixed plate so activating a small mechanism. With a constant potential difference of 500 V between the plates, determine

(a) the force between the plates when they are 5 mm apart;
(b) the force between the plates when they are 2 mm apart;
(c) the work done by the transducer in changing position from (a) to (b); and
(d) the energy supplied from the source during the movement.

Question 4

Figure T7.6 illustrates an electrostatic actuator which consists of a cylindrical outer conductor of inner radius $R = 1$ cm; a cylindrical inner conductor of radius $r = 0.5$ cm; and a dielectric piston of relative permittivity $\varepsilon_r = 3.0$ which can move into the air space between the conductors. A potential difference of 50 kV is maintained between the inner and outer conductors.

Given that the capacitance between two concentric cylinders of radii R and $r(R > r)$, of length L and separated by a dielectric of relative permittivity ε_r is:

$$C = \frac{2\pi\varepsilon_r\varepsilon_0 L}{\ln\,(R/r)}$$

determine the force acting on the dielectric piston.

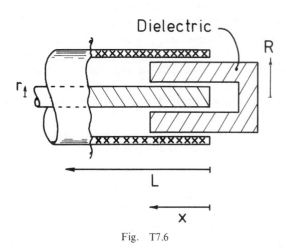

Fig. T7.6

Question 5

A simple electrostatic microphone is made up of two parallel plates each of area A and separated by a distance d. One plate is fixed and the other is free to move in a direction at right angles to the plane of the plate. A sinusoidally varying sound wave impinging on the free plate causes it to oscillate with a frequency f and a maximum displacement from the mean, x (where $x \ll d$). If the plates are maintained at constant charge Q, show that the time-varying component of potential difference between the plates is given by

$$V = \frac{Q}{\varepsilon_0 A}\,x \sin 2\pi\,ft$$

Question 6

An air-spaced variable capacitor set to 0.0015 μF is charged to a potential difference of 500 V and then disconnected from the source. The separation of the plates is then changed, so that the capacitance is 0.0005 μF. Determine:

(a) the energy stored in the capacitor in the initial condition;
(b) the potential difference between the plates in the new position;
(c) the energy stored in the capacitor in the new position; and
(d) the mechanical work done by the electrostatic system during the change in plate separation.

Question 7

An air-spaced variable capacitor is set to a capacitance of 0.001 μF and is connected to a 400 V supply. Without disconnecting the supply the plates are allowed to move closer together so that capacitance is increased to $0.003 \, \mu\text{F}$. Determine

(a) the energy stored in the capacitor before and after the plates are moved;
(b) the charge on the plates before and after the movement;
(c) the energy supplied by the source; and
(d) the mechanical work done by the capacitor.

Question 8

A parallel-plate capacitor has two plates each of area $50 \, 10^{-4} \, \text{m}^2$ separated by a 2 mm thick sheet of mica of relative permittivity 5. The capacitor is charged to a potential difference of 500 V. Determine

(a) the electric field strength in the mica;
(b) the flux density in the mica;
(c) the energy stored per cubic metre in the mica; and
(d) the force per square metre on the plates.

T7.7. ANSWERS AND SOLUTIONS

1. The capacitor is in a constant charge condition. As the plates separate the capacitance decreases

$$\therefore V = \frac{Q}{C} \text{ increases}$$

$$W_e = \tfrac{1}{2}QV \text{ increases}$$

$$D = \frac{Q}{A} \text{ is constant}$$

$$E = \frac{D}{\varepsilon_0} \text{ is constant}$$

2. As the plate separation increases, capacitance decreases

$$Q = CV \text{ decreases}$$

$$W_e = \tfrac{1}{2}QV \text{ decreases}$$

$$E = \frac{V}{d} \text{ decreases}$$

$$D = \frac{Q}{A} \text{ decreases}$$

3. (a) $F = \tfrac{1}{2}E^2 \, \varepsilon_0 A = 8.86 \, 10^{-4} \, \text{N}$
   (b) $F = 55.5 \, 10^{-4} \, \text{N}$
   (c) The work done equals the change in stored energy,
   Energy stored in position (a), $W_a = \tfrac{1}{2}C_a V^2$
   Energy stored in position (b), $W_b = \tfrac{1}{2}C_b V^2$

   $$\text{Work done} = \frac{1}{2}V^2 \varepsilon_0 A \left[\frac{1}{b} - \frac{1}{a}\right] = 66.5 \, 10^{-7} \, \text{J}$$

   (d) The source supplies equal amounts of energy to the field and to the mechanical system:
   Source input $= 133 \, 10^{-7} \, \text{J}$

4. Energy stored in the device is $\tfrac{1}{2}CV^2$
   i.e.

   $$W_e = \frac{1}{2} V^2 \left[\frac{2\pi\varepsilon_0(L-x)}{\ln R/r} + \frac{2\pi\varepsilon_0\varepsilon_r x}{\ln R/r}\right]$$

   The force exerted by the piston in the direction of increasing x is:

   $$F = \frac{dW_e}{dx} = \frac{1}{2} V^2 \frac{2\pi\varepsilon_0}{\ln R/r} \left[-1 + \varepsilon_r\right] = 0.2 \, \text{N}$$

5. $$C = \frac{\varepsilon_0 A}{(d + x \sin 2\pi f t)}$$

   $$V = \frac{Q}{C} = \frac{Q}{\varepsilon_0 A} (d + x \sin 2\pi f t)$$

6. (a) $187 \, 10^{-6} \, \text{J}$ (b) 1500 V
   (c) $562 \, 10^{-6} \, \text{J}$ (d) $375 \, 10^{-6} \, \text{J}$

7. (a) $80 \, 10^{-6} \, \text{J}$ and $240 \, 10^{-6} \, \text{J}$
   (b) $0.4 \, 10^{-6} \, \text{C}$ and $1.2 \, 10^{-6} \, \text{C}$
   (c) $320 \, 10^{-6} \, \text{J}$
   (d) $160 \, 10^{-6} \, \text{J}$

8. (a) $2.5 \, 10^5 \, \text{Vm}^{-1}$ (b) $11.10^{-6} \, \text{C m}^{-2}$
   (c) $1.38 \, \text{J m}^{-3}$ (d) $1.38 \, \text{Nm}^{-2}$

CHAPTER 15

Electrostatic generators

15.1 INTRODUCTION

Interest in electrostatic generators has grown considerably over the last two decades. This has been partly due to the increasing demand from industry for high-voltage supplies and partly due to the pioneering work of research teams in France, Great Britain and the USA. Twenty years ago the major use for electrostatic generators was in the field of particle accelerators and X-ray machines. The electrostatic machine had the advantages of simplicity, ease of control and good regulation, and it did not require auxilliary equipment such as transformers, rectifiers and smoothing circuits which most electromagnetic systems had. As high-voltage technology developed, the demand for supplies to run paint-sprayers, flocking machines, mineral and particle separators and other new processes led to further developments in electrostatic machines, but the big prize was still not taken. It seemed that nobody could produce a machine that could compete directly with the electromagnetic generator.

The difficulties are of course formidable. In Chapter 9 we concluded that the electrostatic machine could not compete with the electromagnetic machine because the required values of electric field strength were unattainable. However, the comparison was a little superficial and a closer examination gives grounds for more optimism. The point is that if we base the comparison on the energy stored in the working gaps the electromagnetic machine wins hands down, but the volume of the working gap in the electromagnetic machine is a very small portion of the total machine volume. In the electrostatic machine the volume of the working gap is much, much closer to the total machine volume and if we now compare machines of equivalent total volume we find that the rating of the volumes of the working gaps can approach 100:1 in favour of the electrostatic machine. In a recent design study by the General Electric Company of New York it is suggested that a high-voltage, direct-current, electrostatic generator could now be built which would compete with existing HVDC power sources. The design was for a 200 kV, 7 MW generator.

There are two types of electrostatic generator, one works by charge transfer and the other is basically a variable capacitance machine. We shall now look at each of these in turn.

15.2. THE CHARGE TRANSFER MACHINE

The most familiar of these machines is the Van de Graaff generator. The principle of operation is illustrated in figure 15.1. If a positive charge is pushed against the direction of action of an electric field the mechanical work done appears as an increase in the potential energy of the charge. The charge can now do work and if a conducting path is provided between the points of high and low potential the charge will move along this path appearing as an electric current. In this case the mechanical input power is converted to electrical power in the output circuit.

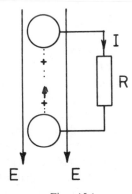

Fig. 15.1

In the Van de Graaff generator illustrated in figure 15.2, the positive charge is moved on an insulating belt which is driven by the mechanical prime-mover. The charge itself is produced by an ionising source. As the charged belt moves into the upper conducting sphere the positive charge is picked up by the collector electrode. The charge then moves to the outer surface of the sphere.

Charge transfer within the top sphere is assisted by the arrangement shown in figure 15.3. The upper pulley

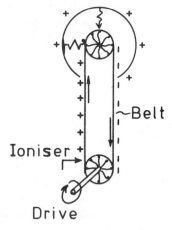

Fig. 15.2

Fig. 15.3

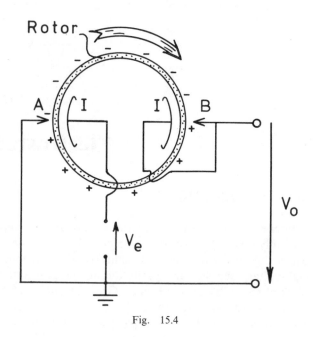

Fig. 15.4

is connected to the collector and as charge flows from the collector to the main sphere a potential gradient is maintained which keeps the collector and pulley at a higher potential than the sphere. This being the case, a discharge at the top ioniser results in electronic charge moving onto the pulley and hence onto the belt. Any positive charge left on the belt is neutralised and excess electronic charge is carried down on the belt to the lower ioniser. The potential of the upper electrode is determined by the amount of charge held on the electrode. As the potential increases, leakage currents flowing from the electrode to earth will increase until the rate of charge leakage equals the rate of charge deposition from the belt. When this happens the potential can increase no further. In the absence of leakage currents the ultimate limit on potential is set by flashover. The flashover voltage can be increased by careful design of electrode assemblies and by enclosing the active part of the machine in very pure hydrogen or an electronegative gas such as sulphurhexafluoride under pressure.

An interesting development of a charge transfer machine is illustrated in figure 15.4. This is a French design which results in a compact, highly efficient and very stable high voltage d.c. generator. The geometry is cylindrical and the figure shows, schematically, a section through the machine. An input ioniser at A discharges under the influence of the exciting potential V_e. Electronic charge is deposited on the surface of the insulating, cylindrical rotor and carried on the rotor to the output electrode at B. Here there is a second ionising electrode and a charge transfer takes place between the rotor and the electrode in much the same way as it does in the top electrode of the Van de Graaff machine. The concept is simple. The success of the machine comes from the imaginative engineering used in the design. Inside the rotor, and between the rotor and the conducting plates (I), there is a low-conductivity glass cylinder. This is inserted to avoid local concentrations of electric field and the clearance between it and the rotor is a few thousandths of an inch. The whole is enclosed in hydrogen under pressure at about 20 atmospheres. The hydrogen gives good electrical insulation, effective cooling and low mechanical losses. In addition it ensures good charge transfer at the ionisers because of the high mobility of the ions.

The machine does not have to be restricted to the two-pole arrangement of figure 15.4. A four-pole arrangement would have input assemblies like A at the 9 o'clock and 3 o'clock positions and the output electrodes would be in the 12 o'clock and 6 o'clock positions. Each set would operate electrically in parallel.

Output control is exercised by monitoring the output voltage and using any error signal to control the exciting potential. This is an essential part of the machine because an electrostatic generator at constant excitation tends to be a constant current source. The more usual applications are for constant voltage output and exciter control is then necessary.

15.3 THE VARIABLE CAPACITANCE MACHINE

In equation T7.8 we established that the force between two charged surfaces was given by

$$F = -\tfrac{1}{2}V^2 \frac{dC}{dx}$$

If we move two charged surfaces apart, against a force such as this, we increase the potential of the charges and they can then do work in an electric circuit which is connected between the surfaces. The amount of work done is clearly a function of the force F and this in turn depends on the manner in which the capacitance of the system varies with position. This is the basic principle of the variable capacitance generator.

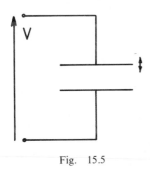

Fig. 15.5

To illustrate the effect, consider figure 15.5 in which one plate of a parallel-plate capacitor is moved up and down as shown in such a way that the capacitance at any instant is given by

$$C = C_0 + \frac{C_1}{\sin \omega t}$$

With a potential V applied, it follows that the charge on the plates will have a time-varying component,

$$Q_1 = \frac{VC_1}{\sin \omega t},$$

There is therefore a time-varying current in the capacitor. If a diode, d_1, is introduced into the circuit, as in figure 15.6, current will only pass through it on that part of the cycle in which point a is positive with respect to b. For the rest of the cycle the diode is reverse-biased and the bottom plate of the capacitor will go negative with respect to b. The second diode, d_2, now becomes forward biased and positive charge flows from the output capacitor to the main, variable capacitor. As a result, a potential difference is built up across the output capaci-

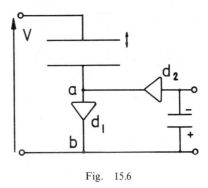

Fig. 15.6

tor. If a load is connected across the output it can be supplied with a continuous current.

A rotary-motion machine would obviously be more useful for the kind of application we have in mind. It would be easier to arrange for a smooth variation of capacitance with time in a rotary machine, not only because the movement is continuous and smooth, but also because the plates can be shaped to give progressive changes in capacitance. The simplest form of machine would have segmented rotor and stator discs arranged as in figure 15.7. The varying capacitance exists between the rotor and the stator and the output connections would be made between rotor and stator.

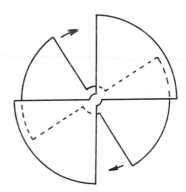

Fig. 15.7

The General Electric design takes this idea a stage further and in so doing removes the need to make an electrical connection to any moving parts. In figure 15.8 the stator has two separate parts and these form the 'plates' of the variable capacitor. The capacitance variation is achieved by spinning a conducting rotor between the stators. When the rotor blades lie completely within the stators the capacitance between stators is a maximum. The total capacitance is then made up of the series combination of stator-rotor-stator capacitance. The capacitance is a minimum when the rotor blades lie outside the stator. A practical machine will have many

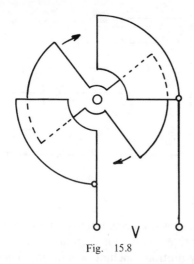

Fig. 15.8

discs on one shaft, all connected electrically in parallel. This will increase the current output. To increase the output voltage several machine units could be connected electrically in series.

To make such a machine an attractive alternative to the electromagnetic alternator and rectifier system it would have to be designed close to the limits of present technology. The overriding concern is with electrical insulation. The machine would have to be operated in high vacuum, but even vacuum breaks down under high electric field strength and techniques will have to be found to improve the performance of insulating gaps in vacuum. Nonetheless the design exercise carried out at General Electric suggests that there is a future for high-voltage, direct-current, electrostatic generators.

FURTHER READING

The Vacuum-Insulated, Varying Capacitance Machine, S. F. Philp, *IEEE Trans. on Electrical Insulation*, Vol. E1–12, No. 2, April 77.

CHAPTER 16

Diagnostic test

The purpose of the following three tests is to give you an opportunity to diagnose your own weaknesses—if any. The first test should be done under examination conditions. Allow yourself 20 minutes and do not refer to notes or to the textbook. Tests 2 and 3 should be done as 'open-book' examinations, i.e. use notes, books or colleagues as needed to get the correct answers. Should you not finish test 1, or should you get the wrong answer, your mistake will become apparent to you as you work through tests 2 and 3.

TEST 1

A coaxial cable has a central conductor 2 mm in diameter encased in polythene insulation. The outer conducting sheath has an inside diameter of 6 mm.

Given that polythene insulation will break down electrically when the electric field strength at any point in the material exceeds 10^7 Vm^{-1}, calculate the maximum voltage that in theory could be applied between the inner and outer conducters.

TEST 2

Take ε_0 as $\dfrac{10^{-9}}{36\pi}$ Fm^{-1}

1. The plates of a parallel-plate capacitor are separated by a distance of 1 mm, and the space between the plates is filled with polythene.

   (a) Assuming a uniform electric field between the plates, calculate the electric field strength in the polythene when a voltage of 10^3 V is connected across the plates.
   (b) The breakdown strength of polythene is 10^7 Vm^{-1}. Calculate the maximum voltage that could be applied across the capacitor without causing insulation failure.

2. Carry out the following integrations:

(a) $\displaystyle\int_{\infty}^{r} \frac{1}{x^2}\,dx =$

(b) $\displaystyle\int_{r}^{a} \frac{1}{x}\,dx =$

3. Write down an equation describing Gauss' law in terms of: the normal component of electric field strength E_n at a point on a closed surface; an elemental area of the surface dS; the charge Q enclosed by the surface; and the permittivity of free space, ε_0.

4. The normal component of electric field strength E_n is constant at all points on a closed surface of area A. The ambient material is air. Write down an equation for the total charge enclosed by the surface.

5. An isolated point charge of 10^{-12} coulombs is situated in air. Calculate the electric field strength E at any point distance 10^{-2} m from the point charge.

6. A long cylindrical conductor has a uniformly distributed static charge of q coulombs per metre along its length. Indicate, by means of one or more sketches, the distribution of the electric field about the conductor. Your sketches should show the distribution of lines of force and the distribution of equipotential surfaces.

7. A long cylindrical conductor has a uniformly distributed static charge of 10^{-12} coulombs per metre along its length. The conductor is situated in air. Calculate the electric field E at a radial distance from the axis of the conductor equal to 10^{-2} m. (Assume that the radius of the conductor is less than 10^{-2} m.)

TEST 3

Take ε_0 as $\dfrac{10^{-9}}{36\pi}$ Fm^{-1}

1. A uniformly distributed, constant electrostatic field has a field strength of value E at all points in any

horizontal plane. The line of action of E at any point is in a vertical direction. A charge q is placed on a horizontal plane.

(a) Write down the equation for the electrostatic force acting on the charge q.

(b) In which direction does this force act?

(c) The charge q is allowed to move a distance d under the influence of the electric field. What is the magnitude of the work done to this movement?

2. Write down an equation defining electric potential in terms of the work done (WD), moving a charge (Q) within a uniform field.

3. A unit charge is moved an elemental distance δx *against* the force due to an electric field E.

(a) Write down the equation for the small amount of work done in moving the charge through the distance, δx.

(b) Write down the equation for the small increment in potential produced by moving the unit charge through the distance, δx.

4. A unit charge is moved from point a to point b against the force due to an electric field E. The magnitude of the electric field E is different at each position between points a and b.

Write down the equation, in integral form, for the potential between points a and b.

5. An isolated point charge q is situated in air.

(a) Write down the equation for the electric field strength E at a point distance r from the positive charge.

(b) A positive unit charge is placed at distance r away from the point charge q. Write down the equation for the force acting on the unit charge.

(c) The unit charge is now moved a distance δx closer to the point charge. Write down the equation for the small increase in potential δV caused by moving the unit charge through the distance δx.

(d) A unit charge is initially placed 1 metre away from the point charge q. It is then moved to a point 0.5 metre away from the point charge. Calculate, in terms of q, the increase in potential produced by moving the unit charge from the point distance 1 metre from q to the point 0.5 metre distance from q.

6. A coaxial cable has a central conductor 2 mm in diameter, solid polythene insulation 2 mm thick and an outer conducting sheath. The inner conductor has a uniformly distributed charge of 10^{-6} coulombs/metre along its length. Calculate the potential difference between the inner and outer conductors. (Take the relative permittivity of polythene as 3.6.)

CHAPTER 17

Task 8: The magnetic field

T8.1 INTRODUCTION

This first task on electromagnetism starts with some simple ideas that should be familiar to you and progresses fairly rapidly to consider forces acting on current-carrying conductors in a magnetic field. In a way it is superficial because nothing is 'proved' and, for example, you are asked to use the idea of flux density without it being fully defined. And yet in another way, it is fundamental in as far as the ideas that are presented are based on experimental fact.

There are two broad aims behind this Task. One is to bring you once again to a realisation of the three-dimensional nature of the electromagnetic field. The other is to bring you rapidly to a consideration of one of the most important of the many electromagnetic phenomena—the interaction between electric current and the magnetic field.

T8.2 OBJECTIVES

When you have completed the Task you should be able to do the following:

(a) sketch approximate patterns to represent the magnetic flux about long straight conductors and coils;
(b) apply correctly the convention that defines the positive direction of the magnetic field produced by a conducting loop carrying a current;
(c) determine the magnitude and direction of the force acting on an element of current $I\delta l$ placed in a uniform magnetic field of flux density B;
(d) visualise the nature of the forces acting on current-carrying loops and conductors of various shapes placed in magnetic fields; and
(e) use the right-hand-screw rule correctly.

T8.3 PRIOR KNOWLEDGE

It will be assumed that you have already been intro-

duced to the basic concepts of magnetism and in particular to the concept of magnetic flux. Most of you will have carried out, or witnessed, experiments using iron filings to 'plot' the magnetic flux around bar magnets and current-carrying conductors and it is with this kind of plot that we begin.

T8.4 BASIC MAGNETISM

Iron filings sprinkled loosely onto a sheet of paper, under which there is a bar magnet, will form themselves into a regular pattern of the sort illustrated in figure T8.1.

A similar pattern is obtained when the bar magnet is replaced by a loop of wire carrying a direct current, provided that the plane of the loop is at right angles to the axis of the magnet as shown in figure T8.2.

The final example, shown in figure T8.3, is the magnetic 'flux' in a horizontal plane about a vertical conductor carrying a direct current.

Fig. T8.1

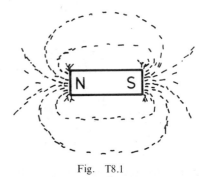

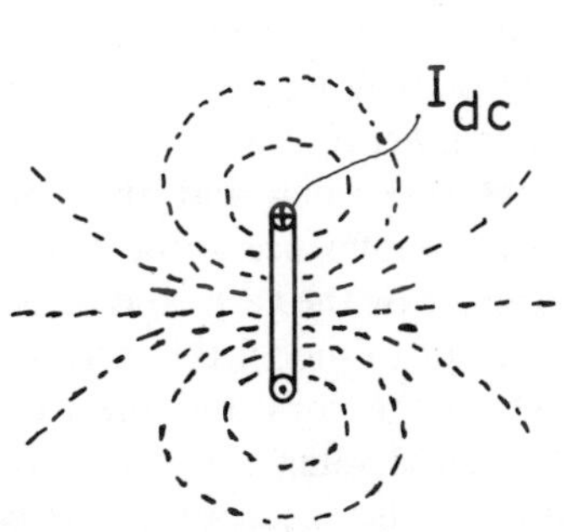

Fig. T8.2

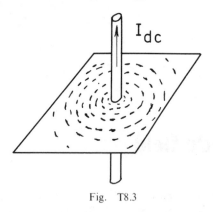

Fig. T8.3

There is a better way of investigating the nature of the field distribution and this is by means of 'exploring coils'. These are small coils through which direct current can be passed and they can be mounted so that they are free to rotate. If we suspend such a coil so that it is free to rotate about a vertical axis and then bring it close to a vertical current-carrying conductor we find that the coil experiences a torque due to the interaction of the current in the coil and the current in the main conductor. Under the action of this torque, the coil aligns itself so that the conductor lies in the plane of the coil. Several such coils mounted in the same horizontal plane and at the same radius from the axis of the vertical conductor will align themselves in the manner shown in figure T8.4 and we

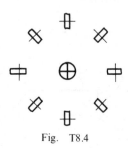

Fig. T8.4

notice that the line joining the centres of the coils defines a circle. A small compass needle placed at any part on the circle will point along the circle, if we ignore the effects of other influences, and we realise that the iron filings, the exploring coils and the compass are all responding to some influence, some 'field' that has been established in space by the vertical conductor.

Our first attempt to model this field is to say let the lines along which the coils and the iron filings point represent a magnetic flux, or flow, which we shall imagine existing in the space about the conductor and about the bar magnet.

T8.5 A SIGN CONVENTION

We can see the need for a convention when we reverse the direction of the current flow in the vertical conductor. The compass needle and the exploring coils all turn through 180°, but the pattern of the field remains the same. There is clearly a right and a wrong direction for the flux flow associated with a current-carrying conductor.

The convention we adopt is this: we say that the positive direction of the magnetic flux is at a right angle to the plane of the exploring coil acting in such a sense that if an observer looking at the coil sees the current in the coil circulating in a clockwise direction then the flux will be directed away from him. This is illustrated in figure T8.5.

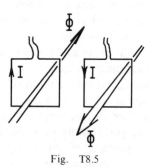

Fig. T8.5

The flux pattern in a horizontal plane through a long, straight vertical conductor carrying a direct current is represented in figure T8.6. We notice from this, and from earlier figures, that there is a tendency for the flux lines to be more densely packed in some regions than in others. We can represent this effect by the idea of a 'flux density', B, which defines the amount of flux crossing a unit area. Flux density is a vector quantity which we shall look at a little more closely later. For the moment let us accept it as defined here.

A final point before we move on: the lines of magnetic flux are continuous. They have no beginning and no end. This is apparent from figure T8.6.

Fig. T8.6

T8.6 FORCE ON A CURRENT-CARRYING CONDUCTOR LYING IN A PLANE WHICH IS PERPENDICULAR TO THE LINE OF ACTION OF A UNIFORM MAGNETIC FIELD

The first point to make is that our current-carrying conductor is not producing the main, uniform field. We shall assume that somehow, someone has produced a magnetic field in which all the flux lines are parallel and in which the flux density B is the same at all points. Into this field we place a long straight conductor so that it lies in the plane which is perpendicular to the line of action of the magnetic field. Figure T8.7 illustrates the case.

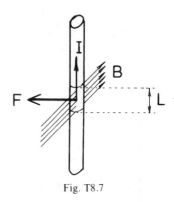

Fig. T8.7

Experimental observation will now show us that a force is exerted on the conductor when a current I flows in it. The magnitude of the force is found to be proportional to the magnitude of the current, the magnitude of the flux density and the length of the conductor in the field. Thus:

$$F \propto ILB$$

We can account for the constant of proportionality by making the following definition:

When a conductor of length 1 metre carrying a current of 1 ampere experiences a force of 1 newton as a result of its position in a uniform magnetic field, the magnitude of the flux density in the plane at right angles to the current is 1 tesla (T). Thus:

$$F = ILB \qquad \text{(T8.1)}$$

The force acts along a line perpendicular to B and I and its direction is obtained by the right-hand-screw rule, rotating the line representing the direction of positive current flow towards the vector B in the shortest way.

Question 1

Deduce the directions of the forces on each conductor element δl shown in figure T8.9. Assume that the mag-

netic field about each conduct is unaffected by the currents flowing in the other conductors.

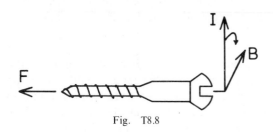

Fig. T8.8

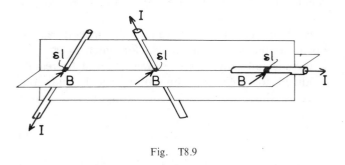

Fig. T8.9

T8.7 FORCE ON A CURRENT-CARRYING CONDUCTOR WHICH IS NOT AT RIGHT ANGLES TO THE MAGNETIC FIELD

The simplest case to consider is shown in figure T8.10. The current I and the flux density vector B both lie in the zy plane with an angle α between them. If we again rely on experimental observation we will find that the magnitude of the force on the conductor length L is given by

$$F = ILB \sin \alpha$$

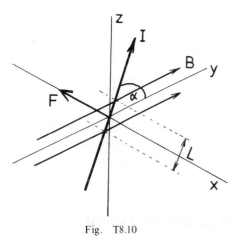

Fig. T8.10

The force again acts perpendicularly to I and B and the direction is again determined by the right-hand-screw rule. The essential difference between equations 1 and 2 is the sin α term in 2. If we were to rotate the conductor in figure T8.10 in the zy plane so that, at any instant 't', sin α was given by sin ωt, we would find the force vector changing magnitude according to the equation

$$F = ILB \sin \omega t$$

but the positive sense of F would remain in the $-x$ direction. Admittedly, the force would act in the $+x$ direction for part of the time as $ILB \sin \omega t$ went negative, but the essential point is that the force would always be along the x axis. Compare this with the previous case in which, as the conductor rotates in the plane perpendicular to B, the force remains constant in magnitude but variable in direction.

Equation T8.2 in fact represents the general case. It obviously includes equation T8.1 for which α $= 90°$, but it includes all other cases as well and can be readily modified to allow for non-uniform fields and conductors which are not long and straight. The correct form is

$$\delta F = I \delta l B \sin \alpha \qquad \text{(T8.3)}$$

which defines the force δF acting on an elemental length of conductor δl in which a current I is flowing and about which there is a flux density B. The angle α is the angle between the line of current flow through δl and the vector B, as in figure T8.11.

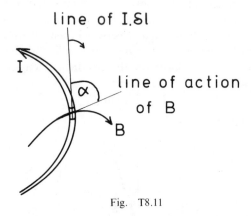

Fig. T8.11

Figure T8.12 gives an indication of how involved real problems can become when the field pattern is not simple. In this case the rectangular loop will be subjected to complex twisting forces.

T8.8 SELF-ASSESSMENT QUESTIONS

Question 2

Determine the nature of the forces acting on the two current-carrying conductors shown in figure T8.13. (Figure T8.6 may help.)

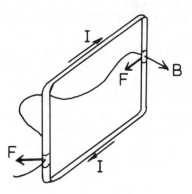

Fig. T8.12

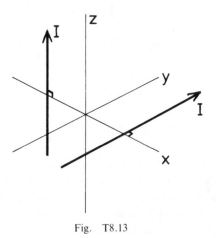

Fig. T8.13

Question 3

Sketch the lines of magnetic flux as they might appear in a plane surface pierced at right angles by two conductors carrying current (a) in the same direction and (b) in opposite directions.

Question 4

A charge q moves with velocity u across a uniform magnetic field of flux density B. Show that the force on the charge is given by $F = quB$.

Question 5

A beam of electrons moves with velocity u along the x axis of a rectangular co-ordinate system. Uniform electric and magnetic fields exist along the y and z axes respectively. Show that the beam passes through the system without deflection if the beam velocity $u = E/B$.

Question 6

A conducting loop in the form of a flat square of side L carries a current I. The loop is suspended vertically as in figure T8.14. Determine the nature of the forces acting on the loop and obtain expressions in terms of IL and B for any torques acting on the loop when the plane of the loop is (a) perpendicular to and (b) parallel to a horizontally directed uniform magnetic field of flux density B.

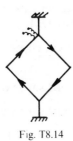

Fig. T8.14

Question 7

Repeat question 6 for a flat circular loop of radius r.

Question 8

Figure T8.15a shows a lightweight wire stirrup pivoted at A_1A_2 and free to rotate around the line A_1A_2. A weight of 0.025 N is attached to the middle of the bottom bar and a vertical flux density of 0.25 T exists in the region of the stirrup. Determine the magnitude of current required in the stirrup to raise it to the position illustrated in figure T8.15b.

T8.9   ANSWERS AND SOLUTIONS

1. The forces are shown in figure T8.16.

2. Figure T8.17(a) shows a plan view of the arrangement of conductors. The field due to the vertical conductor is circular in a horizontal plane. At points a and b the force on the horizontal conductor is vertically upwards, at c and d it is vertically downwards. The conductor will tend to rotate about the y axis. You can visualize what happens as the conductor begins to rotate quite simply by laying two pencils down as illustrated in figure T8.17b to represent B and I at point a. Tilt the right-hand pencil upwards to show the effect of the conductor rotating. Note how the slope of the plane through the two pencils changes and imagine the force vector at right angles to I and B

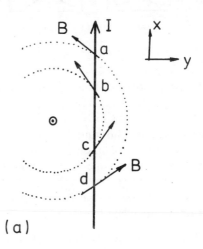

(a)

(b)

Fig. T8.17

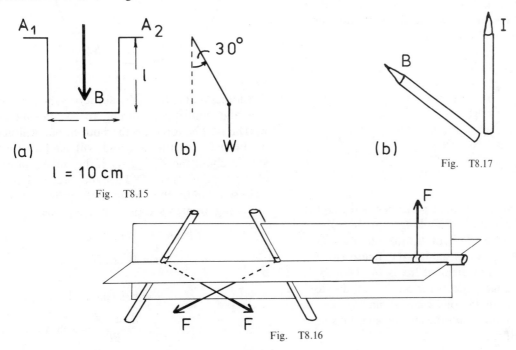

A₁   A₂

30°

B

l

(a)   (b)   W

l = 10 cm

Fig. T8.15

F

F   F

Fig. T8.16

tilting away from the vertical. With the '*I*' pencil sloped at 30° to the horizontal, the force vector should be directed somewhere over your left shoulder.

A similar effect occurs with the conductor in the region *cd* and the nett effect is to impart a lateral movement to the conductor in the direction of decreasing *y*. If the vertical conductor were fixed and the horizontal one were left free, this would rotate about *y* and at the same time slide along the *y* axis until it could lie alongside the vertical conductor with the two currents flowing in the same direction.

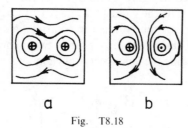

a   b

Fig. T8.18

3. See figure T8.18.
4. The charge *q* moves distance δl in a time $\delta l/u$, and can be thought of as a current $I = q/dlu$.
   The current element is $I\delta l = q.u$
   and the force, $F = I\delta l\, B = quB$
5. The electrostatic force on one electron is *E.e*.
   The magnetic force on one electron is *euB*.
   If the fields are at right angles, the forces are along the same line of action. If the forces oppose, then no deflection occurs when $Ee = euB$.

6. With the flux density vector perpendicular to the plane of the coil, as in figure T8.19, the forces on the sides all lie in the same plane and the nett effect on the coil is zero, provided the coil is rigid.

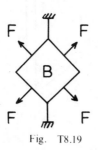

Fig. T8.19

When the flux density acts across the face of the coil, the forces on the sides are no longer in the same plane and there is a resultant torque on the coil. Consider one side of the coil, as shown in figure T8.20. The force on the current element $I\delta x$ is $I\delta xB \sin 45°$ directed into the page. The torque on the coil due to this force is $I\delta xBy \sin 45°$, or $IB \cos 45 \sin 45 x\delta x$.

The total torque due to all the elements in the side of length *L* is $\frac{1}{4}IBL^2$.

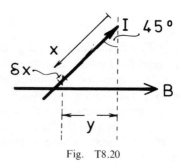

Fig. T8.20

There are four such lengths to account for, so the total torque is IBL^2 or IBA.

7. The force on the current element $I\delta x$ in figure T8.21 is given by:

$$F = BI \sin \alpha \delta x$$

$$= BI \sin \alpha r\delta\alpha$$

Torque due to $F = BI \sin^2 \alpha r^2 \delta\alpha$

$$\text{Total torque} = BIr^2 \int_0^{2\pi} \sin^2 \alpha \, d\alpha$$

$$= BIr^2\pi = BIA$$

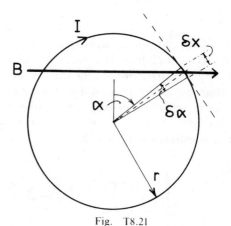

Fig. T8.21

8. The forces on the two sides act across the plane of the coil and contribute nothing to the raising of the weight *W*. The force on the bottom bar will act out of the plane of the coil and will tend to turn the stirrup about the A_1A_2 axis. If the current flows 'out of the page' in figure T8.15(b) the force will be in the right sense to lift the stirrup to the position shown.

Taking moments about the A_1A_2 axis:

$$Fl \cos 30 = Wl \sin 30$$

$$F = W \tan 30$$

but

$$F = BIl, (\sin \alpha = 1)$$

$$\therefore I = \frac{W \tan 30}{Bl} = 0.58 \text{ A}$$

CHAPTER 18

Navigators all at sea
Don't eat onions for their tea
Not that they're at all emetic
They make the compass nonmagnetic

Fact, they say, is stranger than fiction. Who for example would dream up a regulation that 'steersmen, and such as tend the Mariner's Card are forbidden to eat Onyons or Garlick, lest they make the index of the poles drunk.' And yet it is a fact that before the 16th century sailors and others believed that onions and garlic could destroy the magnetic effect of lodestone. One of the earliest experimental scientists, John Baptista Porta, went to great lengths to disprove this particular old wives' tale, eating quantities of onions and garlic and then breathing and belching over the lodestone only to conclude that this 'did not stop its virtues'. Such an experiment now seems absurd, but in the sixteenth century world of Porta scientific enquiry was in its infancy and superstition was rife. It was still believed, for example, that lodestone actually fed upon iron.

The development of the science of magnetism is similar to that of other so-called natural philosophies in its time scale. To begin with, thousands of years of ignorance and superstition; then one or two attempts by intellectual giants to bring order out of the chaos; and finally a growing interest in the subject leading to an explosion of ideas and theories from several great minds within one generation.

The strange properties of magnetite, or lodestone, were certainly known to the ancient Greeks and the material was referred to in Greek literature as early as 800 BC. In Plato's time the phenomenon of magnetic attraction and induction was well enough recognised for him to be able to use it as an analogy in his writings, but it would appear that they did not know of the magnetic compass. The early Greeks believed that lodestone had a soul and that magnetism was divine in nature. Later philosophers suggested that there was something in the iron that the lodestone could feed upon—an idea that persisted into the 16th century world of Porta.

The origin of the magnetic compass seems to be uncertain. The first known reference in Europe occurred in the writings of a twelfth century English monk and in fact some historians argue that the compass was first developed in Europe, probably in Italy, and that its use spread from there. Against this, Dunsheath, in his *History of Electrical Engineering*, refers to an earlier history which dates the first compass as 2637 BC. In that year the Chinese Emperor Hoang-ti is supposed to have built a chariot which carried a female figure which always pointed to the south. The same source refers to an account by a Chinese historian in the 2nd century BC, which describes navigation aided by floating needles.

The magnetic compass leads us nicely to the first of our intellectual giants for in 1269 AD there appeared a description of a mariner's compass enclosed in a case and complete with a 360° degree scale. This was the work of Pierre Pelerin de Maricourt, alias Peter Peregrinus. His is the first known thesis on experimental physics and the results of his work on magnetism are still with us. He took a block of lodestone and had it carved into a sphere. He then used small, pivoted needles of iron to trace out the magnetic field about the sphere. The results we know; he found that the iron positioned itself along imaginary lines that appeared to circle the globe of lodestone in the way in which we imagine lines of longitude to circle the earth. The two crossing points he defined as North and South poles by analogy with the geographic poles.

The next truly significant advance was made by William Gilbert who published *De Magnete* in the year 1600. This famous work contained the results of all his experiments, his interpretations of his own findings and the sum of all that was reliably known about magnetism at that time. The work was without parallel and of particular significance because of Gilberts own philosophy. He relied only on experience. That which could not be demonstrated could not be trusted. He repeated the work of Peter Peregrinus, but had the

69

imagination to realise that what was true for a magnetised sphere could be true for the earth and so became the first person to state with authority that the earth itself was one vast magnet. And yet, despite his seemingly objective scientific method, his final explanation of magnetic attraction was that the lodestone had a soul. The poet John Dryden wrote of him:

> Gilbert shall live till lodestones cease to draw
> Or British fleets the boundless ocean awe.

The magnetic unit which bore his name became the Ampere-Turn with the introduction of the SI system of units.

After Gilbert, ideas developed slowly. It became accepted that there was some kind of magnetic fluid which permeated materials and that too much or too little of it gave rise to a magnetic pole. By 1778 it was considered necessary to have two fluids: one for each type of magnetic pole. The two fluids were mutually attractive, but elements of the same fluid were mutually repulsive. In 1750 the inverse–square law for the force between magnetic poles was put forward by John Mitchell and in 1785 his ideas were confirmed by Charles Coulomb. Coulomb also took up the idea of two magnetic fluids but argued that the fluids were not free to flow. They were, he reasoned, bound to individual molecules and magnetism occurred when these two fluids collected at opposite ends of the molecule. The scene was now set for the great explosion.

André Ampère had been born in 1775, the mathematician Poisson in 1781, and 1791 was to see the birth of Michael Faraday.

Poisson adopted Coulomb's ideas of polarisation in molecules and developed a full mathematical theory for magnetisation. But even while it was being developed his theory was outdated by developments elsewhere. A Danish professor, Oersted, made the simple discovery that a compass needle could be deflected by an electric current. Note, that until this time, 1820, current electricity and magnetism had not been related. The news of Oérsted's work stimulated Ampère's imagination and within a matter of months he had developed a full theory which described the behaviour of current-carrying conductors in magnetic fields and which stated quite clearly the equivalence of a current loop and a small bar magnet. The age of electromagnetism had begun.

In the meantime Michael Faraday was continuing with his own experiments. If Oersted could produce magnetism from electricity then Faraday could produce electricity from magnetism, and he finally did, in 1831. It took a little longer than expected because Faraday, and everyone else for that matter, was looking for a direct current effect. What he finally found was that a sudden change in a magnetic field caused a current transient. This took place on 29th August. By 28th October he had the first d.c. generator working, a machine we now know as Faraday's disc.

A young mathematician, James Clerk Maxwell, now steps into our story. In 1855 he takes upon himself the responsibility of translating Faraday's brilliant experimental work into a coherent mathematical theory. Within ten years he has, with tremendous insight, realised that a changing electric field can produce a magnetic field and has also taken an incredible step into the unknown with his theoretical predictions about electromagnetic waves. It took the experimental scientists until 1887 to prove him right, by which time he was dead.

CHAPTER 19

Task 9: Magnetic flux density

T9.1 INTRODUCTION

In the previous Task I asked you to accept that there was such a thing as a magnetic field and that it could be defined, in part, by a magnetic flux density vector, B. We shall now look more closely at what this is and we shall concentrate on the relationship between it and electric current. This is one of the fundamental relationships of electromagnetism and was first demonstrated by Professor Oersted in 1820. The subsequent work of André Ampère led to a fuller understanding of the nature of the forces between current-carrying conductors and as a result of this work we now see that all magnetic effects, including the effect of the bar magnet, can be ascribed to the action of electric currents.

T9.2 OBJECTIVES

When you have finished this Task you should be able to do the following:

(a) define magnetic flux density in terms of the force acting on a current-carrying conductor;
(b) explain how the concept of flux density enables us to describe the influence of a current on another remote current;
(c) define magnetic field strength in terms of magnetic flux density;
(d) explain, to the satisfaction of your colleagues, the difference between field strength and flux density; and
(e) answer correctly the self-assessment questions.

T9.3 THE MAGNETIC FORCE BETWEEN TWO LONG PARALLEL CURRENT-CARRYING CONDUCTORS

Let us put theory aside for one moment and imagine that we could carry out an experiment together on the two-conductor system illustrated in figure T9.1. As we switched on the currents I_1 and I_2 (both d.c.) we could

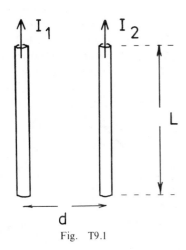

Fig. T9.1

demonstrate easily that a force existed between the two conductors. We could also show that the force was only present when the currents were on and that it acted in a sense to pull the conductors together. With a little more care we could demonstrate that the magnitude of the force on conductor 2 was proportional to:

(a) the length of the conductor;
(b) the magnitude of the current I_1;
(c) the magnitude of the current I_2; and
(d) the reciprocal of the perpendicular distance between the conductors.

Question 1

Write down the equation that describes the force in terms of the above variables.

We here define our constant of proportionality as $\mu_0/2\pi$, where μ_0 is the permeability of free space and we thus have the equation for the force on conductor 2:

$$F_2 = I_2 L \frac{\mu_0 I}{2\pi d} \qquad \text{(T9.1)}$$

Now, compare this with the equation for the force acting on a conductor of length L, carrying a current I_2, in a magnetic field of flux density B, when the angle between the current vector and the B vector is $90°$. This is:

$$F_2 = I_2 L B \qquad \text{(T9.2)}$$

It is apparent then that the effect of the current I_1 on the current I_2 is the same as the effect of a magnetic field of flux density B, with B defined as above, i.e.

$$B = \frac{\mu_0 I_1}{2\pi d} \qquad \text{(T9.3)}$$

If we were to repeat our experiment with I_2 at various positions on a circle of radius d about I_1 we would observe that the magnitude of the force remained constant and that it always acted to pull I_1 and I_2 together. The vector B would therefore always seem to act at a right angle to I_2 and at a right angle to the radius joining I_1 and I_2, as shown in figure T9.2. This would confirm our initial ideas about the nature of the magnetic field about a long straight conductor as suggested in figure T8.6.

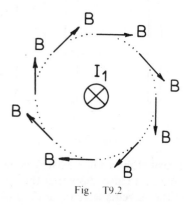

Fig. T9.2

The definition of B in equation T9.3 gives us a better understanding of what the magnetic flux density really is. It is a measure of the influence of an electric current at a remote point. In this case, a measure of the influence of I_1 at the points occupied by I_2. The influence is only felt by other currents, or moving charges, but it is there for as long as I_1 is flowing. Now, why restrict our discussion to the effect of I_1? What about I_2?

Question 2

Write down an equation for the flux density due to current I_2 in figure T9.1, a distance d from the conductor.

Question 3

What is the equation for the magnetic force on the conductor of length L carrying the current I_1 in figure T9.1?

A word of warning! The distribution of the magnetic field depends upon the geometrical arrangement of the current-carrying conductors. Equation T9.3 only holds for the case of the long, straight, cylindrical conductor. What we must do now is to make our approach more

general. A first step would be to appreciate that what is true for a conductor of length L is true for an element δl. So that we could write the force acting on an elemental length of conductor 1 in figure T9.1 as:

$$F = I_1 \delta l B \qquad \text{(T9.4)}$$

It is often useful to think of $I\delta l$ as one parameter—a current element.

T9.4 MOVING CHARGE AND THE MAGNETIC FIELD

The force between two static charges is defined by the inverse–square law of electrostatics. If however charges are moving, an additional force comes into play. It is this force that is the basis of the magnetic effect. This magnetic force is much smaller in magnitude than the electrostatic force and one might therefore wonder why it is that the magnetic forces dominate the electrostatic forces in current-carrying circuits. The answer is that in a conductor there is a balance of positive and negative charge so that the resultant electrostatic effect is zero, but the magnetic effects of charge movement, as current flows, are cumulative.

We can therefore say that the flux density vector that we have defined in the previous section results from the movement of electric charge. This much should be obvious from the experimentally observed relationship between the magnitudes of the flux density and the current. It is possible to reduce equation T9.1 to a form which defines the force as the sum of a series of elemental forces each of which is due to the force between one pair of elemental charges in the two conductors. From this analysis the theoreticians deduced the following basic relationship:

For the system of moving charges defined in figure T9.3

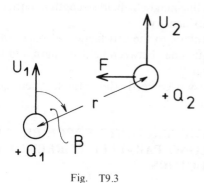

Fig. T9.3

the magnitude of the magnetic force on Q_2 due to Q_1 is proportional to

(a) the magnitudes of Q_1, Q_2, u_1 and u_2;

(b) the inverse square of the distance r; and
(c) $\sin \beta$
Hence,

$$F = K \frac{Q_1 Q_2}{r^2} u_2 u_1 \sin \beta \qquad \text{(T9.5)}$$

where K is a constant. Note that u_1 and u_2 are velocities which are defined with respect to a stationary observer.

Suppose the charge Q_2 is in fact the moving charge contained in an elemental length δl of a conductor carrying a current I_2. Then the charge Q_2 will pass across the end surface of the small length δl in time δt where

$$\delta t = \frac{\delta l}{u_2}$$

the current

$$I_2 = \frac{Q_2}{\delta t} = \frac{Q_2}{\delta l} u_2$$

or

$$I_2 \delta l = Q_2 u_2 \qquad \text{(T9.6)}$$

Hence

$$F = I_2 \delta l \frac{K Q_1 u_1 \sin \beta}{r^2}$$

and by comparison with equation T9.4 we can see that the flux density can be defined as

$$B = \frac{K Q_1 u_1 \sin \beta}{r^2}$$

the constant is

$$\frac{\mu_0}{4\pi}$$

so that

$$B = \frac{\mu_0}{4\pi r^2} Q_1 u_1 \sin \beta \qquad \text{(T9.7)}$$

The line of action of B is perpendicular to the plane containing the vector u_1 and the line r. The direction is defined by the right-hand-screw rule, rotating the vector u_1 towards the vector r. Figure T9.4 defines B for the

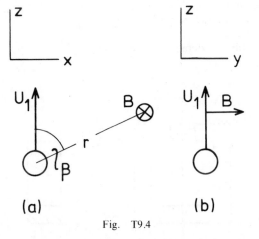

(a)   (b)

Fig. T9.4

case illustrated in figure T9.3, with diagram (a) showing the view along the y axis and (b) the view along the $-x$ axis.

Equation T9.6 can also be used to define a current element $I_1 \delta l = Q_1 u_1$, so that equation T9.7 can be written as:

$$B = \frac{\mu_0}{4\pi r^2} I_1 \delta l \sin \beta \qquad \text{(T9.8)}$$

This is known as the Biot-Savart law and it enables us to calculate the flux density about current-carrying conductors of complex shape. But we shall come back to this in a later Task.

T9.5   MAGNETIC FIELD STRENGTH

Let us return to equation T9.3 and rewrite it as

$$\frac{B}{\mu_0} = \frac{I_1}{2\pi d} = H \qquad \text{(T9.9)}$$

H is defined as the magnetic field strength. It is useful to us because it has a remarkable property. If we take a closed contour, such as shown in figure T9.5, and

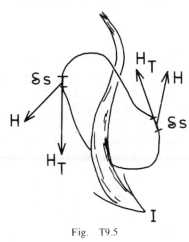

Fig.   T9.5

calculate the product $H_T \delta s$ for each element of length δs around the contour, where H_T is the component of H tangential to δs, then the sum of the elements $H_T \delta s$ around the contour is equal to the total current crossing the surface bounded by the contour. Mathematically, we write:

$$\oint H_T ds = I \qquad \text{(T9.10)}$$

This law is known as Ampère's circuital law, or the magnetic circuit law. We shall return to it later; for the moment let us be content to define H in terms of B and note that because of the relationship in equation T9.10 the units of H are amperes per metre (A m^{-1}). It is useful to think of H as the link between current and flux density and imagine that the current establishes a magnetic field strength H which in turn produces a magnetic flux density B. It can also be helpful to think of H as a magnetic potential gradient so that $\int_0^L H \, ds$ along a path length L defines a magnetic potential difference.

T9.6 SELF-ASSESSMENT QUESTIONS

Take μ_0 as $4\pi \ 10^{-7}$ Hm^{-1}

Question 4

A long straight conductor carries a current of 10 A and is situated in air which can be considered as free space. Calculate the magnetic flux density at a point 0.5 m from the conductor.

Question 5

A current-carrying conductor of length 1 m is situated in a plane at right angles to a uniform magnetic field. The magnetic flux density is 1 T. Determine the current in the conductor when the magnetic force on the conductor is 5 N.

Question 6

Two long parallel conductors of length L carry equal currents and are separated by a distance d. The force between the conductors is 80 N. The current in one conductor is now doubled, and at the same time the separation of the conductors is increased to $4 \, d$. Which of the following is the force between the conductors?

(a) 10 N
(b) 40 N
(c) 160 N
(d) 640 N

Question 7

An electron, e, travels with a velocity u in a plane at right angles to a uniform magnetic field B. Initially the direction of motion is along a line which makes an angle of 60° with the $-x$ axis as illustrated in figure T9.6. Which of the four diagrams in figure T9.6 correctly defines the magnetic force on the electron?

Question 8

A long straight cylindrical conductor carries a current of 10 A. Determine

(a) the magnetic field strength due to this current at a point p distance 2 cm from the axis of the conductor;
(b) the magnetic flux density at p; and

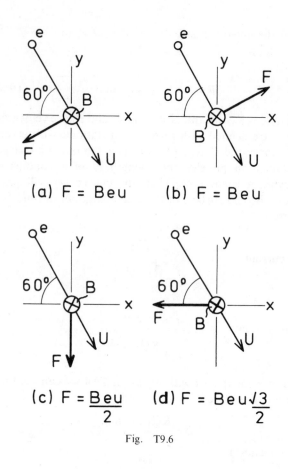

Fig. T9.6

(c) the magnetic force per unit length acting on a second conductor which passes through p and is parallel to the first conductor when the current in each conductor is 10 A.

Question 9

The magnetic flux crossing the airgap of the magnet shown in figure T9.7 is 12 mWb. Determine

(a) the flux density in the airgap;

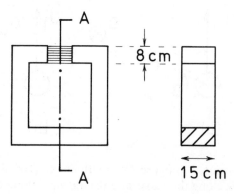

Fig. T9.7

(b) the force on a conductor placed in the airgap so that its length is parallel to the 15 cm side if the current in the conductor is 150 A; and

(c) the magnetic field strength in the airgap.

Question 10

A straight conductor of length 1 m is situated in the plane of a uniform magnetic field and lies at right angles to the field. The magnetic flux density is 1 T and the current in the conductor is 1 A. Which of the following statements best describes the force acting on the conductor? The force on the conductor is:

(a) 1 N, acting along the conductor;
(b) 1 N, acting at a right angle to the field;
(c) 1 N, acting along the field;
(d) 1 N, acting along the field and at a right angle to the conductor;
(e) 1 N, acting at a right angle to the field and at a right angle to the conductor.

T9.7 ANSWERS AND SOLUTIONS

1. $F = KLI_1I_2d^{-1}$, where K is a constant

2. $B = \dfrac{\mu_0 I_2}{2\pi d}$

3. $F = BI_1L = \mu_0 \dfrac{I_1 I_2 L}{2\pi d}$

4. $B = 4 \ 10^{-5}$ T

5. $I = 5$ A

6. $F = 40$ N

7. Diagram T9.6a

8. (a) $H = 79.5$ A m^{-1} (b) $B = 10^{-4}$T (c) $F = 10^{-3}$ Nm^{-1}

9. (a) $B = \dfrac{\Phi}{A} = \dfrac{12 \ 10^{-3}}{120 \ 10^{-4}} = 1$ T

   (b) $F = 22.5$ N

   (c) $H = 79.5 \ 10^4$ A m^{-1}

10. Answer e

CHAPTER 20

The free-space constants

20.1 INTRODUCTION

The system of units used in this book is the system which is generally adopted by engineers and scientists throughout the world. It is known as the Système Internationale, or in abbreviated form, SI. It is based on proposals made by G. Giorgi at the turn of this century for a system of units founded on the metre, the kilogram, the second and one practical unit of electricity. At the time the proposals were made engineers and scientists favoured the centimetre, gram, second or c.g.s. system, even though the electrical units of the system were impractical. The difficulty had been partly resolved by defining practical units for voltage and resistance as 10^8 c.g.s. units and 10^9 c.g.s. units respectively. These were of course the volt and the ohm and since current is the ratio of volts to ohms we can see that what we now call the ampere is equivalent to 0.1 units of c.g.s. current. To further complicate the issue, this collection of c.g.s. units was called the electromagnetic system and a second system called the electrostatic system was in use in which the c.g.s. unit of potential was 300 volts and the unit of current was $1/3 \ 10^{-9}$ amperes. Giorgi's system avoids this confusion because the common units are of a practical size.

In 1948, the International Electrotechnical Commission chose the ampere as the practical electrical unit for the Giorgi system and it then became known as the MKSA system. It became the Système Internationale in 1960 when two further base units were added. These were the Kelvin, for temperature, and the candela for luminous intensity.

20.2 DEFINITIONS OF ELECTRICAL UNITS IN THE SI

AMPERE the ampere is that constant current which, if maintained in two straight parallel conductors of infinite length, of negligible circular cross-section, and placed 1 metre apart in vacuum, would produce between these conductors a force equal to 2.10^{-7} newton per metre length.

VOLT the volt is the difference of electric potential between two points of a conducting wire carrying a constant current of 1 ampere, when the power dissipated between these points is equal to 1 watt.

OHM the ohm is the electric resistance between two points of a conductor when a constant difference of potential of 1 volt, applied between these points produces in the conductor a current of 1 ampere, the conductor not being the seat of any electromotive force.

COULOMB the coulomb is the quantity of electricity transported in 1 second by a current of 1 ampere.

WEBER the weber is the magnetic flux which, linking a circuit of 1 turn produces in it an electromotive force of 1 volt as it is reduced to zero at a uniform rate in one second.

These definitions were adopted by the General Conference on Weights and Measures in 1960.

20.3 THE FREE-SPACE CONSTANTS

The force between two parallel conductors which are separated by a distance d and which carry currents I_1 and I_2 is proportional to I_1 and I_2 and inversely proportional to d. We can write for the force per unit length,

$$F = \frac{K_1 I_1 I_2}{d} \qquad (20.1)$$

where K_1 is a constant.

The units of force in the SI are derived from the base units of mass, length and time since,

$$\text{Force} = \frac{\text{Mass} \times \text{Velocity}}{\text{Time}} = \text{kg m s}^{-2}$$

This unit is the newton.

We now have enough information to determine the magnitude of the constant K_1, but before we do that we should look at the form that K_1 should take. If we leave it as it is then we will find that the constant π occurs in the most unlikely places, such as in the formula for the capacitance of a parallel-plate capacitor. If however we redefine K_1 as $\mu_0/2\pi$, where μ_0 is also a constant, then we obtain:

$$F = \mu_0 \frac{I_1 I_2}{2\pi d} \qquad (20.2)$$

and we find that π occurs only where there is a spherical or cylindrical geometry. This is called rationalisation and the definition of μ_0 as the basic free space constant instead of K_1 makes the SI a rationalised system of units.

From the definition of the ampere we can see that equation 20.2 will yield

$$2 \ 10^{-7} = \frac{\mu_0}{2\pi}$$

or

$$\mu_0 = 4\pi 10^{-7} \text{ henries per metre (H m}^{-1})$$

This is the constant that we have referred to in the previous chapter as the permeability of free space.

The other free space constant that concerns us is the permittivity of free space, ε_0. We shall show in chapter 39 that μ_0 and ε_0 are related by the equation

$$\mu_0 \varepsilon_0 = \frac{1}{c^2}$$

where c is the velocity of light. Thus, having defined μ_0 as $4\pi \ 10^{-7}$, the value of ε_0 is fixed at $8.854 \ 10^{-12}$ farads per metre (F m^{-1}). The previously quoted value of $\varepsilon_0 = 10^{-9}/36\pi$ is thus seen to be an approximation based on the approximation that $c = 3 \times 10^8$ m s^{-1}.

CHAPTER 21

Task 10: The effect of iron on the steady magnetic field

T10.1 INTRODUCTION

Iron has the fortunate property, for us, of being able to multiply the magnetic effect of a current. Put one magnetic rabbit into an iron hat and out pop 10 000 or more. A current-carrying coil which will produce a flux density of 10^{-5} tesla in air could well produce 1 tesla in a magnetic steel. In many ways iron can be thought of as a conductor of magnetic flux, for just as we have an enhanced current flow in a metallic conductor so we obtain an enhanced flux flow in iron and in ferromagnetic materials generally. We use this conducting property to manipulate and guide the flow of magnetic flux. In this way we can create intense magnetic fields where they are of most use to us—in electric motors, generators and transformers.

In this task we shall use our existing knowledge to deduce the behaviour of magnetic materials. We shall show how to allow for the presence of linear magnetic materials in the steady magnetic field and we shall explain why it is that a cycle of magnetism in a magnetic material gives rise to the hysteresis loop.

T10.2 OBJECTIVES

When you have finished this Task you should be able to do the following:

(a) write an essay which will effectively explain to a first year student of electrical engineering how magnetic effects in materials may be attributed to molecular currents;
(b) distinguish between permeability and relative permeability;
(c) explain, to the satisfaction of your colleagues, how relative permeability is used to account for the magnetic effect of a magnetic material;
(d) define normal and incremental permeability; and
(e) write an essay, as in (a), explaining the shape of the B-H loop in terms of the domain theory.

T10.3 PRIOR KNOWLEDGE

The ideas in this Task follow on naturally from our previous work. The questions in Task 8 are relevant and particularly the one that asks you to develop the equation for the torque on a conducting loop in a uniform magnetic field.

T10.4 MAGNETISM

The accepted model of the structure of matter is the atomic model. The basic building block is the atom and this has a relatively heavy positive nucleus and a number of negatively charged electrons in orbit about it. As each electron orbits the nucleus it also spins about its own axis and because of the very high velocities involved these two movements can each be thought of as creating a minute loop of continuous current. In the majority of materials the motion of all the electrons about the atomic nucleus is so ordered that the effects of individual electrons cancel, but there is a small group of materials for which this is not true. To an outside observer, an atom of such material would appear to behave electrically as if it were a small loop of current.

We can deduce, from the work we have done in the previous two Tasks, how these small current loops will behave in the presence of a steady magnetic field. When a steady, uniform magnetic field of flux density B is perpendicular to the plane of the current loop, as in figure T10.1, there is no nett force on the loop. When the flux density vector lies in the plane of the loop, as in figure T10.2, there is a resultant torque on the loop which tends to rotate the loop so that the plane of the loop becomes perpendicular to the magnetic field. The elemental torque on the two elemental strips shown in figure T10.2 is given by:

$$\delta T = 2BI \sin \alpha r \sin \alpha \delta l$$

$$\delta T = 2BIr^2 \sin^2 \alpha \, d\alpha$$

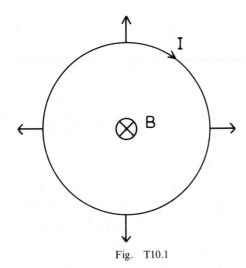

Fig. T10.1

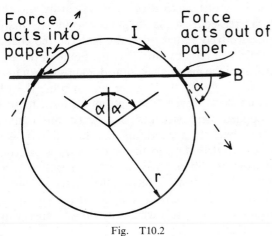

Fig. T10.2

The total torque is then

$$T = 2BIr^2 \int_0^\pi \sin^2 \alpha \, d\alpha = BI\pi r^2$$

In any position, other than that of figure T10.1, there will be a torque on the conducting loop tending to turn the loop in the manner shown in figure T10.2. We note that in the equilibrium position the magnetic field produced by the current loop adds to the main field and this is the effect that we are seeking. As all the current loops in the material align themselves across the externally applied field the total magnetic field is increased considerably. This is the ferromagnetic effect. It is found in soft iron, nickel, cobalt and their alloys. When placed in a magnetic potential gradient these materials give rise to an enhanced magnetic flux density.

T10.5 PERMEABILITY

In free space we have a relationship between the magnetic field strength, H_0, and the magnetic flux density it produces, B_0, defined by:

$$B_0 = \mu_0 H_0$$

In a ferromagnetic material we have an additional component of flux density, B_M, so that the total is

$$B_T = B_0 + B_M$$

We could argue that B_M is the result of a magnetic field strength, H_M, produced by the electronic motion in the atomic structure of the material, so that

$$B_M = \mu_0 H_M$$

and

$$B_T = \mu_0(H_0 + H_M)$$

H_M is often referred to as the magnetisation vector.

Experiment will show us that H_M is related to H_0, but for the ferromagnetic materials which interest us the relationship is not a linear one. It is not possible to write an exact mathematical equation for this, so, for the moment, we shall make an approximation and assume that the relationship is indeed linear, giving

$$H_M = \chi H_0$$

where χ is the magnetic susceptibility of the material concerned.

We can now write

$$B_T = \mu_0(H_0 + \chi H_0)$$
$$= \mu_0 H_0(1 + \chi)$$

or

$$B_T = \mu_0 \mu_r H_0$$

where $\mu_r = (1 + \chi)$ is defined as the relative permeability of the material. It is dimensionless.

The product $\mu_0 \mu_r$ is the permeability of the material concerned. The value of μ_r for soft iron can be as high as 5000, a figure which demonstrates clearly the advantage gained by using ferromagnetic materials whenever large magnetic fields are required.

In passing, let us note that there are some materials for which $\mu_r < 1.0$ and some for which μ_r is slightly greater than 1.0. These are known respectively as diamagnetic and paramagnetic materials. Typical values are: copper, $\mu_r = 0.9999$ and aluminium, $\mu_r = 1.000021$. As far as we are concerned these materials behave magnetically as if they were free space and no further notice will be taken of their presence in the magnetic field.

T10.6 THE DOMAIN THEORY OF MAGNETISM

A domain is defined as a region of material within which all the atoms have aligned magnetic fields. A domain will therefore appear to be a small permanent magnet and there will be a large number of these within the material. The number of domains within a given volume is determined by a complex energy balance within the material. The details of this are outside the scope of this book and we can obtain all we need from the theory by considering the simplified case illustrated in figure T10.3. We shall assume that figure T10.3a shows part of the material when the whole is effectively non-magnetic. As an external magnetic field strength is applied the domains begin to align themselves along the field, so that their magnetism supports the main field.

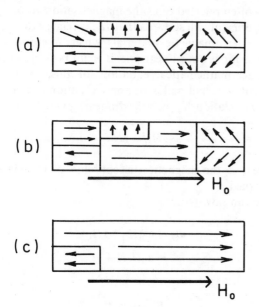

(a)

(b)

(c)

Fig. T10.3

To start with there is a comparatively large increase in magnetism as the domains that are closely aligned rapidly and easily adjust their position. This can be seen in figure T10.3b. As H_0 is increased more domains will align with the field, but it becomes increasingly difficult to produce a change because the remaining domains are so far out of line. If we plot the resultant magnetic flux density against the value of applied magnetic field strength we obtain the familiar magnetisation curve for a ferromagnetic material, similar to figure T10.4. The saturation condition for large values of H_0 occurs because all the domains have been aligned and any further increase in B_T can only come from an increase in B_0.

As we reduce H_0 towards zero we find that the flux

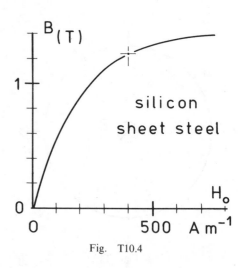

Fig. T10.4

density is reluctant to drop. This is hardly surprising. As we increased H_0 we had to put energy into the material as we effectively restructured the material. To change it yet again will require more energy. Some of the energy comes from the material as some domains return to their original alignments as H_0 falls, but to bring the whole structure back to zero magnetism we have to reverse the applied field strength and force the remaining domains back to a condition in which they make no resultant contribution to the field. As H_0 is varied in a cycle from zero to positive, to zero, to negative, to zero, a plot of B_T against H_0 reveals the hysteresis curve for the material. This we refer to as the B-H loop. We shall interpret it more closely when we deal with energy in the magnetic field.

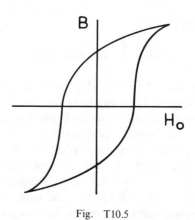

Fig. T10.5

Now, if we had been correct in writing $H_M = \chi H_0$ and $B_T = \mu H_0$, then the plot of B against H would have been a straight line and not a loop. In particular we see that to define μ as B/H is rather meaningless because it can have almost any value between plus and minus infinity. Usually when the term permeability is used it is intended to be the normal permeability which is the ratio of B/H at points along a magnetisation curve. The value of

μ is not constant unless the curve is assumed to be a straight line.

In some applications a small alternating field strength is superimposed on a constant field. The effect is then to produce a small *B-H* loop about the fixed point, as illustrated in figure T10.6. The permeability that the time-varying signal sees is the incremental permeability $\Delta B/\Delta H$.

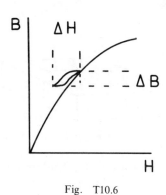

Fig. T10.6

T10.7 SELF-ASSESSMENT QUESTIONS

Question 1

A long straight insulated conductor is positioned in a block of uniform magnetic steel. When the current in the conductor is 10 A the magnetic flux density at a point 0.05 m from the axis of the conductor is 1.0 T. Calculate:

(a) the permeability of the steel, and
(b) the relative permeability of the steel.

Question 2

A toroid, as shown in figure T10.7, is made of a silicon sheet steel and the magnetic field strength in the material is produced by a steady current in the magnetising winding. Given that a magnetic field strength in the

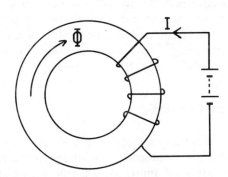

Fig. T10.7

material of 400 Am^{-1} produces a flux density of 1 T calculate the magnetic susceptibility of the steel.

Question 3

Two toroids are manufactured to the same dimensions one from aluminium and the other from silicon sheet steel. In each case a steady magnetic field strength of 400 Am^{-1} is established in the material. Determine the ratio of the flux densities in the two toroids. The magnetisation curve for the steel is shown in figure T10.4.

Question 4

Plot a graph of normal permeability against magnetic field strength using the data from figure T10.4.

Question 5

Write a short note—less than 200 words—to explain how the domain theory accounts for the shape of the *B-H* loop.

T10.8 ANSWERS AND SOLUTIONS

1. The flux density around a long straight conductor is given by

$$B=\frac{\mu I}{2\pi d}$$

Hence

$$\mu=3.14 \ 10^{-2} \ \text{Hm}^{-1}$$

and

$$\mu_r=2.50 \ 10^4$$

2. $\mu_0\mu_r=\dfrac{B}{H}=2.5 \ 10^{-3} \ \text{Hm}^{-1}$

$$\therefore \mu_r=1.99 \ 10^3$$

$\chi=\mu_r-1$, which in this case is indistinguishable from μ_r

3. When H is 400 Am^{-1} in the steel, B_s is 1.24 T. When H is 400 Am^{-1} in aluminium, B_a is $\mu_0 H$ $=5.03 \ 10^{-4}$ T.

$$\frac{B_s}{B_a}=2.47 \ 10^3$$

FURTHER READING

Lectures on the Electrical Properties of Materials, L. Solymar & D. Walsh, Oxford University Press, 1970.

CHAPTER 22

Bubble and squeak

22.1 INTRODUCTION

Modern society makes two very great demands on the electrical engineer. One is for power and the other is for information processing. In meeting these demands the engineer makes extensive use of magnetic materials, often working closely with the materials scientist to push forward the boundaries of what is known and what is possible. At the power end of the spectrum there is a continuing interest in the improvement of materials because the gains to be made are considerable. Generators and transformers are now being built with ratings in excess of 1000 MVA, which is over ten times the rating of QE2's engines. If hysteresis loss in the magnetic core is as low as 0.5 per cent there is still a considerable amount of power being wasted and the problems of cooling the machines are substantial.

At the other extreme, we have magnetic bubble technology. Tremendous developments have been made in this area since the late 1960s and the technology can now offer magnetic bubbles, to those who need them, of about 3×10^{-6} m diameter. Such bubbles are so easy to move about that one million of them could be switched a million times a second with a power input less than one five hundredth of a watt.

A common feature of these extreme applications is the magnetic domain. In fact, the bubble is a magnetic domain which has been isolated and controlled.

22.2 THE MAGNETIC BUBBLE

It is easier to magnetise a ferromagnetic crystal along some axes than along others. These particular axes are known as the preferred magnetic directions and magnetic domains will tend to align themselves along a preferred direction, one way or the other. If we were to slice a thin section from such a crystal so that the parallel, plane surfaces were perpendicular to the preferred direction then the domains would be found to be perpendicular to the surfaces in the manner shown in figure 22.1. An external magnetic field applied along the preferred axis would tend to increase the domains which

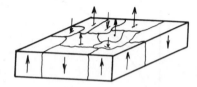

Fig. 22.1

acted in the same sense as the field and decrease those in opposition. A situation similar to that shown in figure 22.2 might then exist. A further increase would bring about an instability in the opposition domains and those in contact with the walls of the crystal would disappear. The ones within the bulk of the crystal would collapse to a characteristic cylindrical shape with a diameter determined by the particular material. Typical diameters would be between 1 and 10 microns. These cylinders are known as magnetic bubbles and remain stable within a range of ± 20 per cent of the critical forming field. The bubbles are mobile and will move under the influence of a magnetic field which has a component parallel to the plane surface of the crystal.

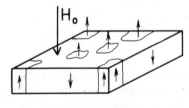

Fig. 22.2

This principle provides us with the basis of a memory system which has no mechanical moving parts, low power consumption and the possibility of direct electronic interfacing. Bubble memories of this kind can be made from wafers of synthetic garnets.

22.3 PROCESSING

Within a bubble memory, information is represented by the presence, or absence, of a bubble; it is therefore a simple binary store. Information is read out via detectors which register the passing of a bubble. The movement of

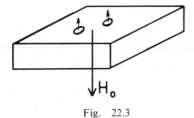

Fig. 22.3

bubbles through the memory is controlled by changing magnetic fields in the plane of the chip. Commercially available memories use rotating magnetic fields to drive bubbles along predetermined paths which are way-marked by carefully placed patterns of magnetic material. Part of such a pattern is shown in figure 22.4 which represents a plan view of a thin bubble chip with the preferred direction of magnetisation into the plane of the paper.

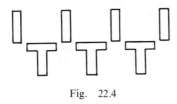

Fig. 22.4

The pattern is produced by depositing Permalloy metal onto the surface of the chip. Permalloy is a low-loss material with a very low coercivity and it can therefore be easily magnetised. A rotating magnetic field acting in the plane of the chip will magnetise the Permalloy and so produce a changing pattern of small bar magnets on the chip surface. Let us assume that the bubble polarity is such that the top of a bubble is attracted to a north pole, then with the external field acting right to left, as in figure 22.5a, a bubble will be located on the left of the T crossbar. As the field rotates clockwise the bubble will follow the moving north pole to the right in the sequence shown in figure 22.5. The effect is that of a simple shift register.

22.4 INPUT, OUTPUT

Bubbles may be produced using the field system described above or by current excitation. In figure 22.6 the bubble generator, G, is a Permalloy disc with a small extension shown in the 1 o'clock position. A magnetic domain is held underneath the disc and, as the field rotates, this domain first expands under the extension and then splits. This releases a small domain, which then progresses to the right as a magnetic bubble. In this case a new bubble is created with each revolution of the external field.

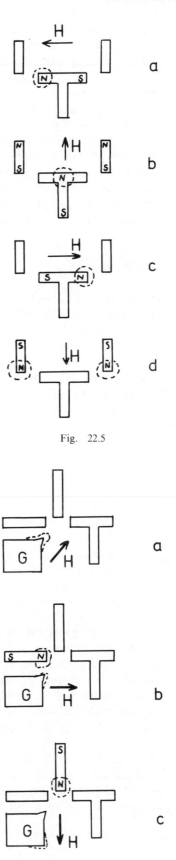

Fig. 22.5

Fig. 22.6

The alternative method is to pass a current pulse through a conducting loop on the surface of the chip. If the polarity of the pulse is correct it will reverse the alignment of the magnetic domain underneath it and this domain will then appear as a magnetic bubble.

The detection system makes use of yet another magnetic phenomenon: that of magnetoresistance. The electrical resistance of some materials, in this case an array of Permalloy, changes in the presence of a magnetic field so that the passage of a magnetic bubble is seen as a change in resistance. By connecting the detector into a bridge circuit it is possible to convert the resistance change into a voltage pulse.

22.5 APPLICATION

A significant feature of the bubble memory is the relative ease with which it can be interfaced with microcomputers. The first commercial chip was a 92 kilobit device that could easily be assembled on the same board as other components in a microprocessor system. The total required storage capacity can be built up of these devices and tailor-made to fit particular needs in microprocessor applications. Within this range of activity the bubble memory has a slight cost advantage over other forms of storage, with the exception perhaps of charge-coupled devices, and as production grows and the technology develops the cost advantage will improve.

22.6 NOISE IN TRANSFORMERS

The direction of magnetisation in a transformer core alternates with the time-varying magnetic field. The alignment of the magnetic domains in the core material is therefore being continuously changed. The domains are physical entities and their continuous re-alignment requires a continuous change in the structure of the material. One extraordinary feature of this is that the material increases in length along the axis of domain alignment. This extension is not very large, perhaps 5 microns in a metre length or 1 thousandth of an inch in 17 feet, but it means that the transformer core is in continuous movement. If the laminations in the core are clamped so that longitudinal changes in length are restricted then transverse vibrations will be established. Both longitudinal and transverse vibrations give rise to audio noise with a fundamental frequency of 100 Hz and significant harmonics up to about 800 Hz. The fundamental has the largest intensity, with the higher harmonics as much as 25 dB down, but the human ear is more sensitive to the harmonic frequencies than to the fundamental so that frequencies above 100 Hz may be the greater source of nuisance.

The change in dimensions of a material with changing magnetic field is known as magnetostriction and this is the major source of audio noise in a transformer.

22.7 NOISE CONTROL

Noise increases with flux density so that a first try at reducing noise might be to run the transformer at a reduced flux density. However, we shall find that the flux in the core is determined by the primary voltage and the turns, assuming that frequency is fixed, so that for a given supply voltage we must increase the cross-sectional area of the core or the number of turns on the winding if we are to reduce the flux density. Both options lead to a larger volume design and greater lengths of steel to vibrate. Overall there is little improvement in noise performance and the disadvantage of greater bulk.

Care in assembly of the core plates can have quite an effect on reducing noise because magnetostriction increases significantly if the material is in compressive stress. Such stresses can be built up in thin sheets of steel simply by squashing them flat. Ideally of course the sheets should leave the steel works perfectly flat and should not then be bent or buckled, but in practice the sheets will be wavy and as they are stacked up to form the laminated core of a transformer the waves will be flattened out. This will cause compressive stress in the sheets and an increase in magnetostriction.

The only satisfactory answer to solving the problem of noise at source is for the materials scientist to produce a steel which is suitable for use in large transformers and which has no magnetostriction. Until then, the transformer manufacturers will continue to work wonders with the materials they have and transmission and distribution engineers will continue hiding some transformers behind walls and in holes in the ground to contain such noise as there is.

FURTHER READING

Magnetic Bubbles, A. H. Bobeck and H. E. D. Scovil, *Scientific American*, June 1972.

CHAPTER 23

Task 11: Ampère's circuital law

T11.1 INTRODUCTION

The circuital law is particularly useful to us in determining the magnetic field strength about current-carrying conductors in certain common geometrical arrangements. Knowing the field strength we can easily determine the magnetic flux density at a point and the magnetic flux around the circuit. The application of the law is straightforward provided that we know the direction of the flux density vector B. It is this proviso that makes the law most useful in situations where the field pattern is predictable.

T11.2 OBJECTIVES

When you have completed this Task you should be able to

(a) state the circuital law in its mathematical form;
(b) understand the meaning of the law sufficiently to enable you to apply it in simple examples;
(c) recognise problem situations which are amenable to solution through use of the law; and
(d) solve problems of the kind shown in the examples and questions in this Task.

T11.3 THE CIRCUITAL LAW

We referred briefly to this in Task 9 when we introduced the idea of magnetic field strength. In the form in which it was introduced, and as it is used here, it holds for the steady magnetic field. If the field is produced by time-varying currents, then the law has to be modified—but more of that later.

The law is a natural law, i.e. it is a statement of fact based on experimental observation. There is little point therefore in attempting a mathematical proof, so let us just accept the law in the following form.

The sum of the product $H_T\delta s$ around a closed path of length s is equal to the current crossing the surface

bounded by the closed path—where H_T is defined as the component of H which is tangential to δs.
i.e.

$$\sum_0^s H_T\delta s = I$$

which in the limit, as δs tends to zero, becomes

$$\oint_0^s H_T\,ds = I \qquad (T11.1)$$

The circle around the integral sign indicates that the integration is about a closed path.

What we must be careful to do now, is get our signs right. We again rely on the right-hand-screw rule. The positive direction for summing $H_T\delta s$ is found by imagining that a right-hand-screw is being screwed in the direction of the current. The rotation of the screw defines the positive direction for summation.

Question 1

Define the positive directions for summing $H_T\delta s$ for the closed paths shown dotted in figure T11.1.

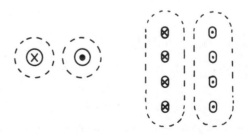

Fig. T11.1

T11.4 USING THE LAW

The law is very easy to use when H_T is constant, because equation T11.1 then becomes:

$$H_T \oint_0^s ds = I$$

85

which gives

$$H_T s = I$$

or

$$H_T = \frac{I}{s}$$

If we need to find H_T at a point, therefore, we must find a closed path of known length, along which H_T is constant and which passes through the point of interest. This implies that we must already have some idea of what the field pattern looks like. A simple example will illustrate the point.

Take the case of the long straight conductor shown in figure T11.2, in which a current I is flowing. We want to know the magnitude of the magnetic field strength at a point distance r away from the axis of the conductor due to the current I. We know that the magnetic field around the conductor will have a cylindrical geometry and that the imaginary lines of magnetic flux will form circles around the conductor. One such circle is shown in figure T11.2. At all points on this circle the flux density, and therefore the magnetic field strength, is constant. The circle is therefore the best path to take when using the circuital law for this particular geometry.

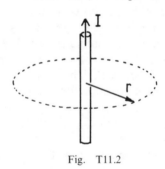

Fig.   T11.2

We then have

$$H_T \oint_0^{2\pi r} ds = I$$

which gives

$$H_T = \frac{I}{2\pi r} \qquad \text{(T11.2)}$$

This gives us a general solution for H at any point about a long straight conductor. We have already assumed in our solution that the field has no component at a right angle to the circular path, so H_T is the total magnetic field strength acting at a point distance r from the long straight conductor.

Question 2

A long straight conductor carrying a current of 10 A lies along the axis of a thin cylinder of sheet steel. The cylinder has a radius of 2 cm and the steel has a relative permeability of 2000. Determine the direction and magnitude of the magnetic field strength, and the flux density, in the steel.

T11.5   EXAMPLE 1

The following examples will show you how to use the law in a variety of cases. There is something to be learned from each one so please work through them carefully and try to solve each problem yourself before proceeding through the worked solution.

A long, flat, copper sheet, 4 cm wide, carries a current of 20 A. Determine the flux density at a point 3 cm from one edge in the plane of the sheet. The case is illustrated by a section through the sheet in figure T11.3. The surrounding medium is air.

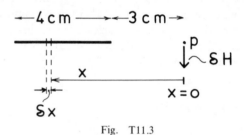

Fig.   T11.3

The flux density can be determined directly from the magnetic field strength, so that the problem essentially is to determine H at the point in question. Although we could probably sketch in the field pattern about the sheet, it is obviously not going to give us an easily defined flux path such as the circle in the previous example. What we must do therefore is break up the sheet into a number of small elements, solve for each element in turn and finally add together the effects of all the elements to obtain the effect of the whole sheet.

If we begin with the thin element δx we can see that as δx becomes very small the element approximates to a long straight conductor. This gives rise to a magnetic field with a cylindrical geometry and we can visualize a circular flux path of radius x centred on the element and passing through the point of interest, p. If we assume that the current is flowing into the paper, then the magnetic field strength at p due to the current element is represented by the vector δH. The current in the element is only a fraction of the total current I and, assuming a uniform current density across a sheet of width W, it is given by:

$$\frac{I}{W} \delta x$$

Using the argument that led to equation T11.2, we can

write:

$$\delta H = \frac{I}{W} \frac{1}{2\pi x} \delta x$$

The effect of the whole sheet is obtained by summing the contributions of all the elements of width δx in the sheet. Thus the magnetic field strength at p is:

$$H = \sum_{x=3\,\text{cm}}^{x=7\,\text{cm}} \frac{I}{W 2\pi} \frac{1}{x} \delta x,$$

which becomes

$$H = \frac{I}{W 2\pi} \int_{0.03}^{0.07} \frac{1}{x} \, dx$$

as δx tends to zero.
Thus,

$$H = \frac{I}{W 2\pi} \ln \frac{7}{3} = 67.4 \text{ Am}^{-1}$$

The flux density can be obtained directly.

T11.6 EXAMPLE 2

A toroid of square cross-section is manufactured from a sheet steel with a relative permeability of 2000. The inner and outer radii of the toroid are 8 cm and 12 cm respectively. A coil of 500 turns is wound uniformly around the ring and carries a current of 1 mA. Determine the total magnetic flux in the toroid.

The geometry is illustrated in figure T11.4. In this case we arrive at a value for flux by calculating the magnetic

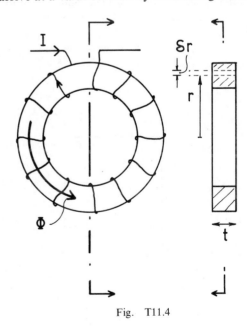

Fig. T11.4

flux density at various points in the steel. This in turn is determined from the values of H given by the circuital law. The flux path is clearly defined for us by the geometry. Flux will flow in circular paths around the toroid in the manner shown in figure T11.4. The flux path defines the line of action of flux density and hence of the magnetic field strength. At a general radius r we can define B_r by the circuital law as follows:

$$B_r = \mu_0 \mu_r H = \mu_0 \mu_r \frac{I}{2\pi r} \tag{T11.3}$$

The current enclosed by the path of length $2\pi r$ is 500×10^{-3} A.

The flux flow across the small area $t\delta r$ is given by

$$\delta\Phi = B_r t \delta r,$$

or

$$\delta\Phi = \mu_0 \mu_r \frac{It}{2\pi} \frac{1}{r} \delta r$$

The total flux in the toroid is the sum of all the elements $\delta\Phi$ in all the small areas $t\delta r$, thus

$$\Phi = \mu_0 \mu_r \frac{It}{2\pi} \int_{0.08}^{0.12} \frac{1}{r} \, dr$$

$$\therefore \Phi = \mu_0 \mu_r \frac{It}{2\pi} \ln 1.5 = 3.24 \text{ } \mu\text{Wb}$$

Note the important difference between this example and the last. In the last one we were interested in the flux density at a point and we summed the magnetic field strength at the point. In this example we are interested in the flux across an area and we sum the contributions of flux across the area.

T11.7 EXAMPLE 3

A long, straight, hollow conductor has inner and outer radii of 1 cm and 2 cm respectively. The conductor carries a current of 1000 A which is assumed to be uniformly distributed across the section of the conductor. Determine the direction and magnitude of the flux density at a general radius r within the walls of the tube.

Figure T11.5 illustrates a section across the tube with inner and outer radii shown as r_1 and r_2. The current is assumed to flow into the paper. At a general radius r, for $r_1 < r < r_2$, a circular path encloses a proportion of the total current. This proportion can be considered as an independent current-carrying conductor. If, therefore, we apply the circuital law to the circular path of radius r we obtain

$$\oint_0^{2\pi r} H_r \, ds = I_e$$

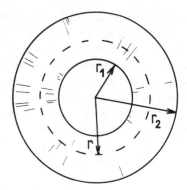

Fig. T11.5

or

$$H_r = \frac{I_e}{2\pi r}$$

where I_e is the current enclosed by the circle of radius r. Assuming a uniformly distributed current,

$$I_e = I \frac{\pi(r^2 - r_1^2)}{\pi(r_2^2 - r_1^2)}$$

so that

$$B_r = \mu_0 H_r = \frac{\mu_0 I}{2\pi r} \frac{(r^2 - r_1^2)}{(r_2^2 - r_1^2)}$$

T11.8 BOUNDARY CONDITIONS

Using the circuital law and the principle of conservation of flux we can deduce the relationship between the magnetic conditions on either side of an interface between two different magnetic materials. In figure T11.6 we apply the circuital law to the dotted path shown.

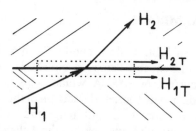

Fig. T11.6

As the small sides of the rectangular path become vanishingly small the circuital law gives us

$$H_{2T} = H_{1T}$$

If we now imagine a very thin flat box, shown in section in figure T11.7, with the larger flat sides on either side of the interface we can say that the flux out of the top surface equals the flux into the bottom surface, or

$$B_{1N} = B_{2N}$$

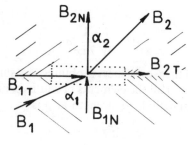

Fig. T11.7

We can also write:

$$\tan \alpha_1 = \frac{B_{1T}}{B_{1N}} \qquad \tan \alpha_2 = \frac{B_{2T}}{B_{2N}}$$

$$\therefore \frac{\tan \alpha_1}{\tan \alpha_2} = \frac{B_{1T}}{B_{2T}} = \frac{\mu_1 H_{1T}}{\mu_2 H_{2T}} = \frac{\mu_1}{\mu_2}$$

and in the special case where material 2 is non-magnetic and material 1 has a large relative permeability

$$\frac{\tan \alpha_1}{\tan \alpha_2} \simeq \infty$$

or

$$\alpha_2 \simeq 0$$

From this we deduce that lines of flux which pass from a ferromagnetic material into air leave the surface of the material at right angles.

T11.9 SELF-ASSESSMENT QUESTIONS

Question 3

A conducting loop *abcd* lies in a plane containing a long straight current-carrying conductor, as shown in figure T11.8. The current in the conductor is 10 A. The loop *abcd* is a plane square with sides of length 2 m. The whole system is in air.

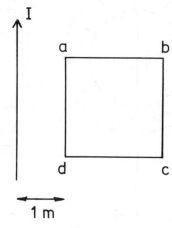

Fig. T11.8

(a) Determine the magnetic flux density at a perpendicular distance X from the conductor, and hence

(b) calculate the total magnetic flux passing across the surface bounded by the loop.

Question 4

Two long conducting plates of width 10 cm are held between two long blocks of iron to form a go-and-return circuit. The plates are insulated from the iron and a current of 100 A flows out along the top plate and returns along the bottom plate. A section through the circuit is shown in figure T11.9. The iron is assumed to have an infinitely large relative permeability.

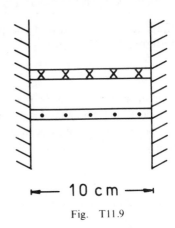

$\longmapsto$ **10 cm** $\longmapsto$

Fig. T11.9

(a) Show that the flux density above and below the two plates is zero, and

(b) determine the value of the flux density in the space between the plates.

Question 5

In the electromagnet shown in figure T11.10, $r_1 = 2$ cm, $r_2 = 3$ cm and $t = 1$ cm. The flux in the airgap

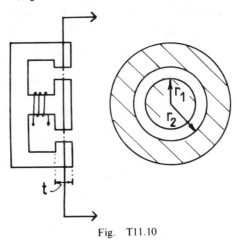

Fig. T11.10

is to be $126 \ 10^{-6}$ Wb and it is assumed that the flux crosses the airgap radially with no fringing. The magnetic material used in the magnetic circuit has a very large permeability.

(a) Determine the maximum and minimum values of flux density in the airgap;

(b) obtain an expression for the flux density in the airgap in terms of the general radius r; and

(c) determine the number of ampere-turns required on the centre limb.

T11.10 ANSWERS AND SOLUTIONS

1. Positive directions are, reading from left to right, clockwise, anticlockwise, clockwise, anticlockwise.

2. The flux in the steel tube will follow a circular path with the centre of the circle on the axis of the cylinder. We can apply the circuital law to this path as follows

$$\oint_0^{2\pi r} H \, ds = I$$

$$H = \frac{I}{2\pi r} = \frac{10}{2\pi \ 2 \ 10^{-2}} = 79.6 \ \text{Am}^{-1}$$

$$B = \mu_0 \mu_r H = 4\pi \ 10^{-7} \ 2000 \ H = 0.2 \ \text{T}$$

3. The flux about the conductor will follow circular paths which are centred on the axis of the conductor. Applying the circuital law to a circular path of radius x gives:

$$H_x = \frac{I}{2\pi x}$$

The flux density at x is, $\mu_0 H_x$.

To obtain the total flux across the surface $abcd$ we must first obtain an expression for the flux across an elemental area and then sum across the whole area. We look for a pattern, or a symmetry, which will help us and we find this from the result of part a. This tells us that B is constant at any distance x from the conductor, so we can draw a line parallel to the side ad, and between ad and bc, and know that B is constant along the line. If the line is a general distance x from the conductor and has a small thickness δx then the element of flux through the line is:

$$\delta \Phi = B_x 2 \delta x$$

the total flux is

$$\Phi = \int_1^3 \frac{\mu_0 I 2}{2\pi x} \, dx = \frac{\mu_0 I}{\pi} \ln 3$$

4. Consider the upper conductor with current flowing into the paper, the flux pattern around the conductor will be as shown in figure T11.11. Given end supports of infinite permeability, the magnetic field strength along the paths marked Y in the iron will be zero.

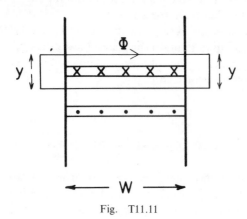

Fig. T11.11

Applying the circuital law to the path shown gives

$$\oint H\,ds = I$$

$$H\,2W = I$$

or

$$H = \frac{I}{2W} \qquad \therefore B = \frac{\mu_0 I}{2W}$$

By symmetry, the flux density about the lower conductor will have the same magnitude. Both values are independent of the dimension Y, thus summing the fields gives zero flux density at all points above and below the plates and a value $2B$ between the plates.

$$2B = \frac{2\mu_0 I}{2W} = 1.26\ 10^{-3}\ \text{T}$$

5. (a) The maximum value of B occurs at $r = r_1$ and is

$$B_{\text{max}} = \frac{126\ 10^{-6}}{2\pi r_1 t} = 0.10\ \text{T}$$

The minimum value of B occurs at $r = r_2$ and is

$$B_{\text{min}} = \frac{126\ 10^{-6}}{2\pi r_2 t} = 0.07\ \text{T}$$

(b) $B_r = \dfrac{\Phi}{2\pi rt}$

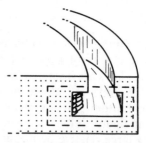

Fig. T11.12

(c) Using the circuital law around the path shown dotted in figure T11.12 we have

$$\oint H\,ds = NI$$

where N is the number of turns on the centre limb carrying a current I. Since the magnetic core has a very large permeability the value of H in the iron is is vanishingly small, therefore

$$NI = \int H\,ds$$

across the airgap, which becomes

$$NI = \int_{r_1}^{r_2} \frac{\Phi}{\mu_0 2\pi t}\frac{1}{r}\,dr$$

$$NI = \frac{\Phi}{\mu_0 2\pi t}\ln\frac{r_2}{r_1} = 647\ \text{A}$$

Note that this is the first example that we have seen in which H was not a constant. We could solve it only because the geometry was such as to enable us to obtain an expression for H in terms of the path length r. If you were able to solve this problem without reference to the solution then you are doing very well indeed.

CHAPTER 24

This is your local displacement current—here is the news

24.1 INTRODUCTION

In our work on magnetism so far we have restricted ourselves to considering the effects of steady electric currents. The world of the electrical engineer is however a world of time-varying current and we now need to decide whether or not what is true for steady current is also true for time-varying current. Ampère's circuital law provides a useful starting point for this study.

24.2 THE INCOMPLETENESS OF THE CIRCUITAL LAW

Equation T9.7 defines the flux density at a point caused by a moving charge. It can be rewritten as:

$$H = \frac{Q_1 u_1}{4\pi r^2} \sin \beta \qquad (24.1)$$

Imagine then a charge Q_1 approaching a circle of radius a along a line perpendicular to the plane of the circle and passing through its origin, as in figure 24.1. The moving charge establishes a magnetic field strength at all points on the circle. This is defined in magnitude by equation 24.1 and in direction by figure T9.4. If the circuital law is applied to the circumferential path around the circle it yields a solution for H which takes into account the effect of all the charges moving along the line in the same sense as Q_1. But suppose Q_1 never reaches the circle. Suppose that Q_1 is travelling along a conductor and that

the conductor ends on one plate of a parallel plate capacitor to the left of the circle in figure 24.1. Equation 24.1 still holds. There is still a magnetic field strength at all points on the circle as the charge approaches the plate, but according to the circuital law, as we have defined it, $\oint H \, ds = 0$ because there is no conduction current passing across the flat, circular area bounded by the path of radius a. In this case the circuital law gives us the wrong answer. In a sense what we have come up against is the question—how do we visualise an electric current, as we understand it, flowing across the insulating gap of a capacitor?—or how do we imagine current flowing from a transmitting aerial through free space to a receiver? The answer is to be found in a new concept which we call displacement current.

24.3 DISPLACEMENT CURRENT

In figure 24.2 a parallel-plate capacitor is being charged by a conduction current I_C. There is no conduction through the capacitor, because there is a thickness of dielectric between the plates, and yet the current I_C exists on both sides of the capacitor and there is clearly some mechanism by which energy is passed through the insulation. Between the plates of the capacitor there is an electric field strength, E; an electric flux density D; and a flux ψ. The conduction current, I_C, is defined as:

$$I_C = \frac{\delta q}{\delta t},$$

where δq is the charge passing a fixed point in the circuit

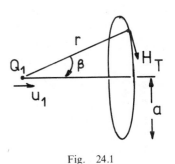

Fig. 24.1

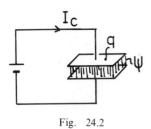

Fig. 24.2

in time δt. Thus, I_C represents the rate of accumulation of charge on the plates. Now, $\psi = q$, so that I_C may be written as

$$I_C = \frac{d\psi}{dt}$$

This is the alternative concept that we need. Instead of attributing the magnetic effect to a conduction current, we attribute it to a rate of change of electric flux. In terms of figure 24.1 we are saying that a portion of the electric flux emanating from Q_1 passes through the circle of radius a. The rate of change of this flux with time produces the magnetic field strength H about the circumference and the circuital law is then written as

$$\oint H \, ds = \frac{d\psi}{dt}$$

We now have two ways of describing the effects of a moving charge: one in terms of conduction current and the other in terms of $d\psi/dt$—a quantity known as displacement current. Where continuous conducting circuits are involved either method can be used, but obviously conduction current is the more convenient model. Displacement current is used where conduction current is clearly not appropriate as for example in determining the magnetic effects in free space of remote, moving charge.

Where there is a combination of effects due to a conduction current and a displacement current the circuital law is written as

$$\oint H \, ds = I_C + \frac{d\psi}{dt}$$

A case is illustrated in figure 24.3 in which the electric flux, ψ, is assumed to be produced by remote charges.

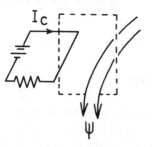

Fig. 24.3

At power frequencies, e.g. 50–60 Hz, the ratio of displacement current to conduction current tends to zero and there is then no need to make any corrections to the theory that we have developed so far. In fact within metallic conductors the conduction current will dominate the displacement current until radio frequencies are reached.

Task 12:   Magnetic circuits

T12.1   INTRODUCTION

Magnetic circuits are used to concentrate the magnetic effect of a current within a particular region in space. In simple terms, the circuit directs the magnetic flux to where it is needed. A magnetic circuit may be constructed from a variety of sections with different lengths and cross-sections and even different magnetic properties. The magnetising characteristics of the materials will be non-linear and design solutions need to take this into account. A typical design problem would be the determination of the current required in a coil to produce a given flux density in the airgap of a small actuator, relay or electromagnet.

T12.2   OBJECTIVES

When you have completed this Task you should be able to do the following:

(a) define magnetomotive force and reluctance;
(b) state the relationship between m.m.f., flux and reluctance;
(c) produce an electric circuit analogue for a magnetic circuit; and
(d) given a magnetic circuit and appropriate parameters, determine the ampere-turns needed to produce a given flux density in the circuit.

T12.3   PRIOR KNOWLEDGE

You should have completed Tasks 10 and 11 satisfactorily.

T12.4   THE MAGNETIC CIRCUIT

The easiest circuit to begin with is the iron ring with airgap, illustrated in figure T12.1. The magnetic flux produced by the current I in the coil of N turns is assumed to follow the circular path shown dotted in the

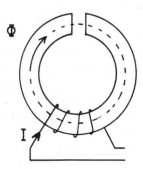

Fig.   T12.1

figure. The flux leaves the iron pole pieces and flows across the airgap without any lateral displacement so that the flux density in the airgap is the same as the flux density in the iron. Let the lengths of the flux paths in the iron and in the airgap be l_i and l_g respectively and assume the permeabilities of iron and air are μ_i and μ_0 respectively.

We now apply the circuital law to the dotted path and obtain:

$$\int H \, ds = NI$$

But H is not constant. The flux density in air and iron is assumed to be the same so that

$$H_i = \frac{B}{\mu_i} \quad \text{and} \quad H_g = \frac{B}{\mu_0}$$

We determine the integral as follows:

$$\oint H \, ds = \int_{s=0}^{s=l_i} H_i \, ds + \int_{s=l_i}^{s=l_i+l_g} H_g \, ds$$

H_i and H_g are each constant when the current in the coil has the steady final value, so that

$$\oint H \, ds = H_i l_i + H_g l_g$$

Normally we would write this equation down immediately without making the intervening step. We now have

$$NI = H_i l_i + H_g l_g$$

or

$$NI = B\left(\frac{l_i}{\mu_i} + \frac{l_g}{\mu_0}\right)$$

or

$$NI = \Phi\left(\frac{l_i}{\mu_i A} + \frac{l_g}{\mu_0 A}\right) \quad \text{(T12.1)}$$

Given the flux, or flux density needed in the gap, the geometry of the ring and the permeability of the iron we can calculate NI.

There are two assumptions that we have made which need to be examined more closely. The first is that all the flux follows the path shown in figure T12.1 and the second is that the flux density in the airgap is the same as the flux density in the iron. In practice a magnetic field will always be established in the medium about the iron core. This is referred to as the leakage field and there is a leakage flux associated with it. The effect is illustrated in figure T12.2 and we can see that the flux produced by the coil, Φ, will be greater than the useful flux in the airgap, Φ_g. An exact calculation of the leakage flux is by no means simple and we tend to rely, where necessary, on experimentally derived coefficients which give the expected ratio of total flux to useful flux for the particular geometry being used. For our purposes we shall assume that we are always dealing with examples in which $l_g \ll l_i$ in which case leakage is negligible.

Figure T12.2 also illustrates the effect of fringing in the airgap. Across the centre of the airgap the flux Φ_g is spread over an area which is greater than the cross-section of the iron. Thus the mean flux density in the gap is less than the flux density in the iron. We again use an empirical correction and assume that the effective area of the gap is that which we would obtain by adding a strip of width $\frac{1}{2}l_g$ around the actual cross-section of the iron. Provided that l_g is small compared with the linear dimensions of the pole piece, then we can assume that fringing is negligible.

T12.5 THE EFFECT OF A NON-LINEAR MAGNETISING CHARACTERISTIC

Equation T12.1 gives a simple solution for NI. Given the required flux Φ we can easily determine B_i and we can then read off H_i from the magnetising curve for the particular material being used. But, suppose we turn the problem around and assume that we have a magnetic circuit with a coil of N turns and we want to know what flux density we would have in the gap when a particular current I exists in the coil. Equation T12.1 will not give us a solution because there are now two unknowns on the right-hand side: one is the flux Φ and the other is the permeability μ_i. The permeability can only be found when we know B_i, but B_i can only be found from Φ and to find Φ we need to know μ_i!

Let us rewrite the equation as follows:

$$NI = H_i l_i + H_g l_g$$

or

$$NI = H_i l_i + \frac{B_i l_g}{\mu_0}, \text{ since } B_i = B_g,$$

$$\therefore B_i = -\frac{l_i}{l_g}\mu_0 H_i + \frac{NI\mu_0}{l_g} \quad \text{(T12.2)}$$

There are two variables, B_i and H_i, and the equation has the form $Y = -mX + c$ which describes a straight line. To solve for B or H we must have a second equation—or relationship—between B and H and this is given in the magnetising characteristic of the iron. We therefore adopt a graphical solution for the two relationships and plot equation T12.2 on the magnetising characteristic in the manner shown in figure T12.3. Where the graphs cross is the solution for B_i and H_i.

Now try the second of the self-assessment questions.

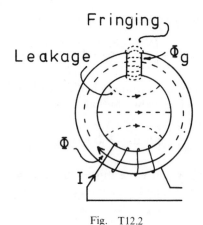

Fig. T12.2

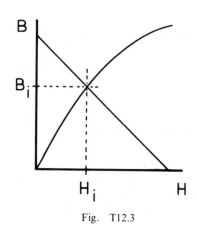

Fig. T12.3

T12.6 THE ELECTRIC CIRCUIT ANALOGUE

Equation T12.1 is similar in form to Ohm's law and we can interpret NI as the potential function, Φ as the flow function and the expression in brackets as the impedance function. NI is known as the magnetomotive force (m.m.f.) and is in fact the quantity defined by the circuital law since

$$NI = \oint H \, ds$$

The impedance function is known as the reluctance of the magnetic circuit and we can see in equation T12.1 that there are two terms—one for each distinct part of the magnetic circuit. An equivalent electric circuit can be drawn as in figure T12.4. Circuits of this kind can be very useful aids in the solution of more complex magnetic circuits, but they should only be used as guides. Unlike the majority of electric circuits that we meet, the circuit in figure T12.4 is non-linear. The value of the reluctance is a function of the flux density in the circuit and the relationship is a complex one. For this reason the use of reluctance in calculations is not recommended.

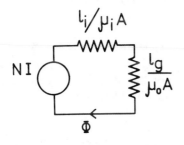

Fig. T12.4

T12.7 AN EXAMPLE

The magnetic circuit shown in figure T12.5 is made of cast steel and a coil of 300 turns is wound on the lower limb. Determine the current needed in the coil to maintain a flux density of 1 T in the upper limb. The magnetisation curve for cast steel is given in figure T12.6.

This is an example in which an equivalent electric circuit is useful. The circuit is shown in figure T12.7. Suppose we had to determine the generator voltage needed to establish a current I_3 in the upper resistance R_3. Our solution might proceed as follows:

(i) from I_3 and R_3 determine the voltage V_3 across R_3;

(ii) knowing that this voltage exists across R_2 as well, determine $I_2 = V_3/R_2$;

(iii) add $I_3 + I_2$ to obtain I_1;

(iv) determine the voltage V_1 across R_1; and

(v) finally calculate $V = V_1 + V_3$.

We follow the same algorithm to determine the ampere-turns on the bottom limb of the magnetic circuit.

(i) $B_3 = IT$ and therefore $H_3 = 930 \text{ Am}^{-1}$ (from the graph). The m.m.f. across R_3 is $930(6+21+6)$ $10^{-2} = 307$ A. (NB we take the mean path length)

(ii) $H_2 = \dfrac{307}{21 \ 10^{-2}} = 1462 \text{ Am}^{-1}$

$\therefore B_2 = 1.3$ T, from the graph and $\Phi_2 = 1.3 \ 3 \ 10^{-2} \ 0.4 \ 10^{-2} = 0.156 \ 10^{-3}$ Wb

(iii) $\Phi_1 = \Phi_2 + \Phi_3 = 0.156 \ 10^{-3} + 0.9 \ 10^{-3}$ $= 1.056 \ 10^{-3}$ Wb

(iv) $B_1 = \dfrac{1.056 \ 10^{-3}}{9 \ 10^{-4}} = 1.17$ T

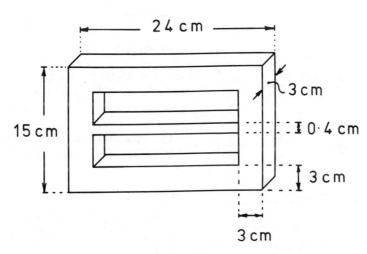

Fig. T12.5

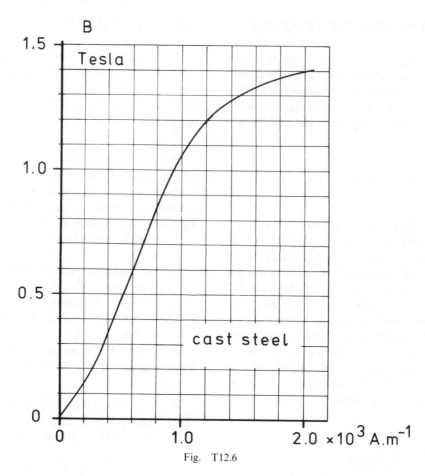

Fig. T12.6

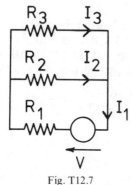

Fig. T12.7

$\therefore H_1 = 1150 \text{ Am}^{-1}$ from graph

$\therefore$ m.m.f. across $R_1 = 1150 \ (6+12+6)10^{-2}$

$= 380 \text{ A}$

(v) total m.m.f. required $= 380 + 307 = 687 \text{ A}$

$\therefore$ current required in 300 turns $= \dfrac{687}{300} = 2.29 \text{ A}$

T12.8 SELF-ASSESSMENT QUESTIONS

Question 1

A coil of 500 turns is wound on a mild steel ring which has a mean circumference of 30 cm and a cross-sectional area of 5 cm². The ring has a 1 mm airgap, in the manner of figure T12.1 and the flux density in the gap is to be 1 T. At this value of flux density the relative permeability of the steel is 1.3 10³. Determine:

(a) the total flux in the core;
(b) the m.m.f. across the airgap;
(c) the m.m.f. across the flux path in the steel; and
(d) the current required in the coil.

Question 2

The magnetic circuit of figure T12.2 has a mean diameter of 30 cm, a cross-sectional area of 10 cm² and an airgap 0.25 cm long. The ring is made of cast steel and is wound with 1000 turns of wire carrying a current of 2 A. The magnetisation curve for the steel is given in figure T12.6. Determine the mean flux density in the ring.

Question 3

In the magnetic circuit represented in figure T12.8 the outer and inner radii of the ring are 20 cm and 15 cm respectively and the ring has a square cross-section. The main pole pieces are of width $W = 10$ cm and thickness

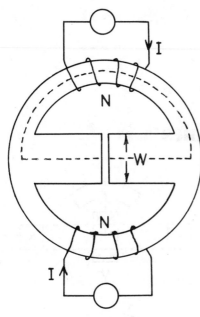

Fig. T12.8

5 cm. The airgap is 5 mm long. The following figures define the magnetisation characteristic of the material used.

B(Tesla)	0	0.7	0.9	1.0	1.1	1.2	1.3	1.4
$H(\mathrm{Am^{-1}})$	0	100	150	180	230	340	500	1000

(a) Assuming that each coil has the same turns and carries the same current, determine the ampere turns required from each winding to produce a flux density of 1 Tesla in the airgap, and

(b) calculate the flux density in the airgap when the ampere-turns from each winding is set to 5570.

T12.9 SOLUTIONS

1. (a) Flux $= BA = 5 \ 10^{-4}$ Wb

(b) m.m.f. across gap $= H_g l_g = \dfrac{B_g l_g}{\mu_0} = 800$ A

(c) m.m.f. across steel $= H_i l_i = \dfrac{B_i l_i}{\mu_0} = 184$ A

(d) Total ampere-turns $= 984$

$$\therefore I = \frac{984}{500} = 1.97 \text{ A}$$

2. Using the circuital law about the mean path, shown dotted in figure T12.2, we obtain

$$NI = H_i l_i + H_g l_g$$

which gives

$$B_i = -\frac{l_i}{l_g} \mu_0 H_i + NI \frac{\mu_0}{l_g}$$

or

$$B_i = -0.47 \ 10^{-3} H_i + 1.0$$

This is plotted on figure T12.6 in the manner of figure T12.3 to give a solution for B at $B = 0.69$ T.

3. (a) Using the circuital law about the mean path shown dotted in figure T12.8, we obtain

$$H_i l_i + H_g l_g = NI$$

from the magnetisation curve, when $B = 1$ T, $H = 180 \ \mathrm{Am^{-1}}$,

$$\therefore 180[\pi \ 17.5 \ 10^{-2} + 35 \ 10^{-2} - 5 \ 10^{-3}]$$

$$+ \frac{5 \ 10^{-3}}{4\pi \ 10^{-7}} = NI$$

$$161 + 3979 = NI$$
$$4140 = NI$$

These are the ampere-turns required on *each* winding.

(b) $H_i l_i + H_g l_g = NI$

gives

$$B_i = -0.23 \ 10^{-3} H_i + 1.4$$

This is plotted on the magnetising curve as a straight line through the points $H = 0$, $B = 1.4$ T and $H = 1000$ A, $B = 1.17$ T, giving a solution for B at $B_i = 1.29$ T.

CHAPTER 26

Some small machines

26.1 INTRODUCTION

Not all electric motors are designed to give continuous rotary motion. The linear motor is one obvious example of this, but there are others. The moving coil in a moving-coil instrument is an electric motor which is restrained so that it will only turn through part of one revolution. Then there are reciprocating machines which go up and down or from side to side and machines which will change position quite accurately in response to current pulses fed from a master controller.

There is little point in attempting to describe the operation of the different types of machine by a common theory even though they all rely on the same fundamental principle that static and moving charges interact to give rise to forces. It is far more useful to explain the behaviour of the machine types in terms of their most obvious characteristics. Thus a machine which is essentially an arrangement of two systems of current-carrying conductors may be best analysed in terms of the forces between current-carrying conductors, while a machine which has one current system and a permanent magnet field may be best described in terms of the LiB relationship. In other cases the law of attraction between magnetised surfaces is most appropriate. In fact the art of engineering analysis lies in finding the most appropriate model for a particular case.

26.2 THE DYNAMOMETER INSTRUMENT

In its simplest form this machine consists of two coils, one of which is fixed while the other can pivot on a central axis. The machine is represented in plan and section in figure 26.1. The fixed coil is the coil X and coil Y is arranged to pivot in the plane which is perpendicular to the plane of X.

A current I_1 in X produces a flux density B in the plane of Y. A current I_2 in Y causes a torque to act on Y given by $T = BI_2A$. (This was proved in question 6 chapter 17.) If coil Y is restrained by a spring then it will pivot until the electromagnetic torque is balanced by the restraining torque of the spring. Let us now express the

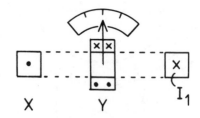

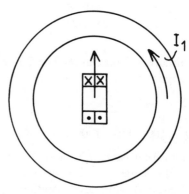

Fig. 26.1

torque in terms of the two currents I_1 and I_2. In the absence of any iron, B is proportional to I_1 so that $T = K_1 I_1 I_2$, where K_1 is a constant. Now let us assume that the currents vary sinusoidally with time and that they are out of phase by an angle ϕ so that instantaneously

$$i_1 = \sqrt{2}I_1 \sin \omega t \quad \text{and} \quad i_2 = \sqrt{2}I_2 \sin (\omega t + \phi)$$

The average torque on coil Y is then the average of the product,

$$2K_1 I_1 I_2 \sin \omega t \sin (\omega t + \phi)$$

which is

$$T_{av} = K_2 I_1 I_2 \cos \phi$$

where K_2 is a constant.

Here then we have the basis of an electric instrument which will produce an average torque, and hence a deflection, proportional to the product of two r.m.s.

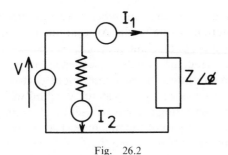

Fig. 26.2

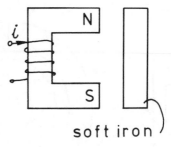

soft iron

Fig. 26.3

values of current and the cosine of the angle between the current phasors. What is it used for?

Referring to figure 26.2, we can write:

$$\text{Power input to the load } Z = P = VI_1 \cos \phi$$

but

$$V = I_2 R$$

so that

$$P = RI_1 I_2 \cos \phi$$

If, then, we pass the currents I_1 and I_2 through the separate coils of our instrument the deflection we obtain will be proportional to the power in the circuit. The instrument can therefore be calibrated as a wattmeter.

26.3 VIBRATORS

Figure 26.3 illustrates an electromagnet and we would expect the soft-iron yoke to be attracted to the core when current flows in the exciting winding. In making this movement the system is attempting to minimise the reluctance of the magnetic circuit. This is equivalent to

maximising the flux linkage of the circuit. If we arrange the core and yoke as in figure 26.4a but restrict the yoke so that it can only move in the y direction the system will still try to minimise the reluctance which it can do by moving the yoke to the position shown in figure 26.4b. Thus, as current flows in the coil the yoke is pulled down and the spring is stretched. When the current is switched off the yoke is pulled back to its original position by the spring. If we apply an alternating current to the coil we can expect the yoke to oscillate in the y direction but at what frequency?

The maximum force of attraction occurs when the current has maximum value, either positive or negative, so that there will be two instances of maximum force and two of zero force in one cycle of a.c. The fundamental frequency of oscillation is thus $2f$ and if the mechanical system is tuned so that its natural frequency is $2f$ we will have a resonance at that frequency. Such a system has been used as the main drive in electric razors.

If we change the geometry of this device and make the coil the moving member and then introduce a permanent magnet we still have a vibrator but the frequency of oscillation is different. The case is illustrated in figure 26.5.

We now find that with the current direction shown in

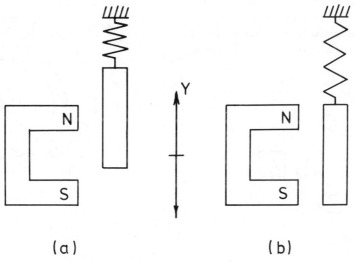

(a)

(b)

Fig. 26.4

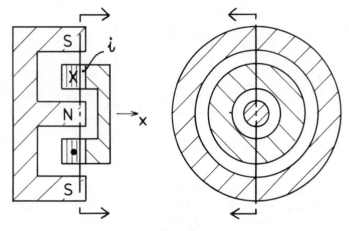

Fig. 26.5

the figure the coil is pushed out of the air gap. A reversal of current pulls the coil back into the gap. The fundamental frequency is thus the frequency of the applied current and we should be able to recognise this machine as the basis of the electromagnetic loudspeaker.

26.4 A RELUCTANCE STEPPING MOTOR

The machine illustrated in figure 26.6 can be thought of as a rotary version of the shaver motor in as far as it moves to decrease the reluctance of the magnetic circuit. It consists of 4 poles which can be excited separately and a five-pole rotor made of high-permeability material. With coil A excited by a direct current, minimum reluctance is obtained when a rotor pole is directly in line with A. This pole is numbered 1. If the current is switched from A to B, minimum reluctance is achieved by the rotor moving so that rotor pole 2 is in line with B. A succession of current pulses applied to coils A, B, C and D in that sequence will cause the rotor to 'step' round in steps of $18°$. The number of poles on stator and rotor can be varied to give machines with different stepping angles. Such devices are useful in applications

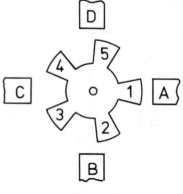

Fig. 26.6

which require an exact number of revolutions, or parts of revolutions to be made. An example is in the automatic control of machine tools.

If we made the switching sequence fast enough we could make the rotor turn continuously. It is easier in practice to make a special stator winding which when fed with alternating current will set up a rotating m.m.f. wave in the airgap of the machine. The vector of maximum magnetic field strength then appears to rotate about the axis of the rotor. If the rotor is then reshaped, as in figure 26.7, it can lock into the m.m.f. pattern and rotate at the same speed. Such a machine can only run at this one speed, called the synchronous speed, and if overloaded will stall. It is not self-starting.

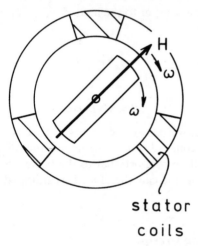

stator
coils

Fig. 26.7

26.5 THE HYSTERESIS MOTOR

This is a small machine which can start itself and which will run up to synchronous speed provided that

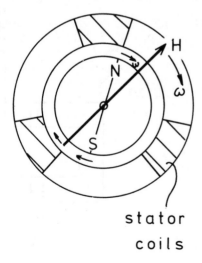

stator
coils

Fig. 26.8

the load torque is not excessive. We again require a stator winding which will provide us with a rotating m.m.f. wave in the airgap, but we now use a rotor material which has a large hysteresis effect. Because of hysteresis, maximum flux density in the iron is achieved somewhat later than the instant of maximum magnetic field strength. Thus as the H vector sweeps around the rotor the peak of induced magnetism in the rotor lags by a small time interval as illustrated in figure 26.8. The magnetised rotor tries to align itself with the line of maximum field strength and a torque is developed. It is interesting that the machine develops an almost constant torque at speeds between zero and synchronous.

FURTHER READING

Electronics & Power, Nov./Dec. 1977.
Small Electric Motors, *Philips Technical Review*, Vol. 33, No. 8/9, 1973.

CHAPTER 27

Task 13: Permanent magnets

T13.1 INTRODUCTION

Permanent magnets are widely used in electromagnetic machines, actuators and meters and perhaps for this reason magnets are often thought of as large devices. The other end of the size range can however be demonstrated by sprinkling iron filings onto a banker's card, or security card, which is magnetically coded. Permanent magnets are also to be found in the information storage world in the form of magnetic tapes and ferrite memory stores. In this Task we shall be introducing the common terms used to describe the characteristic values of permanent magnets and looking at simple techniques for determining the magnetic conditions in magnetic circuits which include permanent magnets.

T13.2 OBJECTIVES

When you have completed this Task you should be able to:

(a) define 'remanence' and 'coercivity' as descriptors of magnetic materials;
(b) determine the flux density in the airgap of a magnetic circuit containing a permanent magnet of known characteristic;
(c) design a magnetic circuit containing a permanent magnet to give a required flux density in an airgap;
(d) design a circuit to maximise the flux density for a given gap volume; and
(e) design for minimum volume of permanent magnet material.

T13.3 A MAGNETISED TOROID

A toroid, of the kind illustrated in figure T11.4, can be magnetised by passing a current through the winding. If the current is increased from zero to a value I_1 and then decreased to zero the magnetisation of the material will follow the portion *oab* of the magnetisation curve shown in figure T13.1—assuming of course that the core

is initially demagnetised. If the current is cycled continuously between plus and minus I_1 the magnetisation cycle for the core will be defined as *abcdea* in figure T13.1.

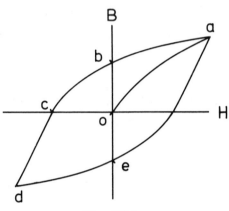

Fig. T13.1

Whenever the applied current is zero there is a finite value of flux density in the core, given by *bo* or *oe*. This is known as a remanent flux density and in this condition the toroid is said to be permanently magnetised. Just how permanent the magnetism is will depend on the magnitude of *oc*. If *oc* is small then the permanent magnetism will be easily destroyed by stray magnetic fields or by mechanical vibration. The magnitude of *oc*, in amps per metre, is known as the coercive force and the larger the coercive force the more permanent the magnet.

As the magnitude of the current I_1 is increased so the area of the *B-H* loop increases until saturation of the core material occurs. The values of *ob* and *oc* are then at their maximum. These maximum values are defined as the remanence and the coercivity respectively and they are characteristic values of the core material. The range of values for coercivity is enormous with soft iron at about 30 Am^{-1} and 'hard' permanent magnet materials as high as 10^5 Am^{-1}.

T13.4 A TOROID WITH AN AIRGAP

Applying the circuital law to this case we obtain:

$$\oint H \, ds = NI$$

or

$$H_i l_i + H_g l_g = NI$$

where the subscripts i and g refer to iron and gap values.

When the current is taken to zero, and a state of permanent magnetism exists in the core, the above equation equates to zero so that

$$H_i = -\frac{l_g}{l_i} H_g = -\frac{l_g B_g}{l_i \mu_0}$$

In this case, let us assume that the effective area of the core, A_i, does not equal the effective area of the airgap, A_g.
Then

$$\Phi_i = \Phi_g$$

and

$$B_g A_g = B_i A_i$$

so that

$$H_i = -\frac{l_g}{l_i \mu_0} \frac{A_i}{A_g} B_i \qquad (T13.1)$$

But, if we are given the dimensions of a circuit and asked to find the flux density in the airgap this equation, by itself, is of no help because it contains two unknowns, B_i and H_i. However, we met a similar case in section T12.5 and decided there that the second equation needed for a solution was contained in the magnetisation curve. The same method of solution can be adopted here, and we simply plot equation T13.1 on the magnetisation loop for the material being used. We must however use the *B-H* loop and not the magnetisation curve because the magnetisation curve does not allow for the hysteresis effect which produces the remanent magnetism. In fact we only require the portion of the loop which relates B and $-H$. This is called the demagnetisation curve.

Question 1

A toroid of square cross-section is manufactured from a magnetic steel. The inner and outer radii of the toroid are 8 cm and 12 cm respectively. An airgap of thickness 1 cm is made in the toroid by a cut in a radial plane. The toroid is magnetised to saturation and the magnetising current is then reduced steadily and continuously to zero. Determine the flux density in the airgap when the toroid is acting as a permanent magnet. The demagnetisation curve for the core material is defined as follows

B(T)		0.7	0.6	0.5	0.4	0.3	0.2	0
$-H(\times 10^3 \ \mathrm{Am}^{-1})$		0	10	20	25	28	30	32

T13.5 OPTIMISATION

The pole pieces of a magnetic circuit are very often shaped so that the cross-section of the airgap is different from the cross-section of the main magnetic circuit. This gives a certain amount of flexibility to the designer. He can for example buy magnets of standard size and adapt them to suit his particular needs by using soft-iron pole pieces. Cost is of course important and a designer may wish to maximise the flux density in a gap of fixed volume or minimise the amount of expensive permanent magnet material. As we examine these possibilities we find that a new parameter emerges—the energy product.

Consider the circuit shown in figure T13.2, and take

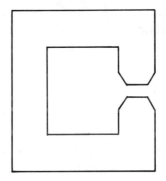

Fig. T13.2

l_i and l_g as the mean path lengths in iron and air, and A_i and A_g as the respective mean cross-sectional areas. Let us decide to keep the gap volume constant at $A_g l_g$ and attempt to maximise the flux density in the gap for a given magnetic material. At first sight one might be tempted simply to reduce the area because for a given flux the flux density is inversely proportional to A. However, we know that the reluctance of the airgap is also inversely proportional to A so that as A decreases, the flux will decrease. Now for the permanent magnet,

$$H_g l_g + H_i l_i = 0$$

or

$$B_g = -\mu_0 \frac{l_i}{l_g} H_i$$

and

$$B_g = B_i \frac{A_i}{A_g}$$

so that

$$B_g^2 = -\mu_0 \frac{l_i A_i}{l_g A_g} H_i B_i \qquad (T13.2)$$

The product $l_g A_g$ is to be kept constant and the product

$l_i A_i$ will hardly vary as l_g is changed because $l_i \gg l_g$, so the maximum value of B_g is obtained when the product $B_i(-H_i)$ is a maximum. Figure T13.3 shows the variation of this product with B and there is a clear maximum. The maximum value of the product is known as the energy product.

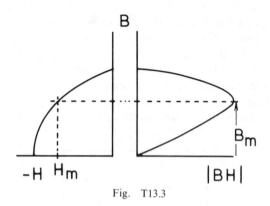

Fig. T13.3

Now let us rewrite equation T13.2 as

$$l_i A_i = -\frac{l_g A_g B_g^2}{H_i B_i \mu_0} \tag{T13.3}$$

This defines the volume of the magnet. Suppose then that we have a design in which l_g and A_g are fixed—possibly to accommodate a standard coil size—and B_g is predetermined from a knowledge of the magnitude of torque we need to develop on the coil when a known current flows in it. We now see that we can minimise the volume of the magnet by making the product $(-H_i)B_i$ a maximum. This occurs when $B_i = B_m$ and $H_i = H_m$ as in figure T13.3. Note that we probably have two values of flux density in our circuit because there is no requirement for B_g to equal B_m, but the flux must be continuous so that

$$A_i = \frac{B_g A_g}{B_m} \tag{T13.4}$$

We must therefore have shaped poles to allow for this change in cross-section—and more, because l_i is defined by equations T13.3 and T13.4 and there is no guarantee that l_i will fit the design. If it does not then the pole pieces are extended to complete the circuit. This is no great disadvantage if pole pieces of soft iron are used.

T13.6 SELF-ASSESSMENT QUESTIONS

Question 2

A permanent magnet is required to establish a flux density of 0.5 T across an airgap of length 3 mm and effective cross-sectional area 5 cm². Determine the minimum volume of suitable permanent magnets made from the following steels:

Sample 1: $(BH)_{max} = -20\,000$ T Am^{-1}; $B_m = 0.6$ T

Sample 2: $(BH)_{max} = -800$ T Am^{-1}; $B_m = 0.5$ T

Question 3

Assuming that the two materials in question 2 can only be purchased in the shape of straight rod, determine the dimensions of the magnets you would order and indicate how you would design the magnet circuit to satisfy the requirements of question 1.

Question 4

Determine the dimension of a permanent magnet designed to satisfy the requirements of question 2 and made from the material specified in question 1.

Question 5

Repeat question 4, but allow for the presence of pole pieces of effective length 12 cm, cross-sectional area 2.5 cm² and relative permeability 800. Neglect leakage and fringing.

T13.7 SOLUTIONS

1. In this case $A_g = A_i$, if fringing is ignored, and equation T13.1 gives $H_i \simeq -1.29 \cdot 10^4 B_i$.
   This is plotted as a straight line on the demagnetisation curve and where the two graphs cross is the solution. This gives $B = 0.62$ T.

2. Sample 1: $l_i A_i = -\dfrac{l_g A_g B_g^2}{H_i B_i \mu_0} \simeq 0.15 \cdot 10^{-4}$ m³

   Sample 2: $l_i A_i \simeq 3.7 \cdot 10^{-4}$ m³

3. Sample 1: $B_i = B_m = 0.6$ T, $B_g = 0.5$ T, $A_g = 5$ cm²

   $\therefore A_i = 4.17$ cm²

   $H_i l_i = -H_g l_g$

   and by substitution

   $l_i = 3.5$ cm

   Sample 2: $A_i = 5$ cm²

   $l_i = 74.5$ cm

The magnetic circuit would have to be completed with pole pieces of low reluctance and an assembly of the sort illustrated in figure T13.4 would be required.

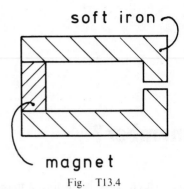

soft iron

magnet

Fig. T13.4

4. By plotting the product $-BH$ against B for the values of BH given in question 1, and drawing the best curve through the points obtained, $|BH|_{max}$ is estimated as $10.4 \ 10^3 \ \text{T Am}^{-1}$ and this occurs when $B_i = 0.46$ T.

$$A_i = \frac{A_g B_g}{B_i} = 5.44 \ \text{cm}^2$$

$$l_i = -\frac{H_g l_g}{H_i} = 5.3 \ \text{cm}$$

5. The solution for $|BH|_{max}$ still holds approximately true so B_i is 0.46 T as before and the cross-section of the magnet is still 5.44 cm^2.

However the circuital law now gives

$$H_i l_i = -(H_p l_p + H_g l_g)$$

where $H_p l_p$ is the m.m.f. required in the pole pieces.

$$H_p l_p = \frac{\Phi l_p}{\mu A_p}$$

and substitution gives

$$H_i l_i = -\frac{1.65}{\mu_0} 10^{-3}$$

and

$$l_i = 5.8 \ \text{cm}$$

CHAPTER 28

Do, do, do, do, do you remember?

28.1 INTRODUCTION

Magnetic materials are the basis of the most flexible memory devices available to modern society. It is now possible to store any kind of information in these devices and to manipulate and recall it at will. Magnetic tape is familiar to most people through their use of cassette recorders for recording and playing back music and it may not be very long before many households have magnetic video recorders to store and playback television programmes. These devices have been available to sound and broadcast engineers for many years.

The use of magnetic recording for storing numerical data is extensive and is presently the method most commonly used by the computer industry. The advantages of magnetic recording stem from its simplicity. The materials used are not particularly difficult to come by, the recording and playback techniques are simple, and the store itself can be changed, corrected or wiped out as required. Apart from deliberate changes, the store is virtually permanent.

Let us then begin by examining a data store of a type used in the computer industry, which is based on the behaviour of small magnetic cores with rectangular magnetisation characteristics.

28.2 MAGNETIC CORE STORES

Figure 28.1 shows a toroidal core threaded by two wires. Each wire acts as a one-turn loop around the core

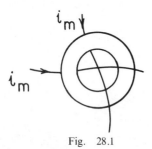

Fig. 28.1

and the assumed direction of positive current is shown in the figure. The core material is assumed to have a

hysteresis loop which can be approximated to the rectangular form shown in figure 28.2. In this case, since H is proportional to the current threading the toroid, the axes of the curve are shown as B and I.

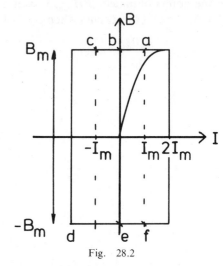

Fig. 28.2

With the core initially demagnetised, a current of magnitude $2I_m$ will drive the core into saturation and as the current subsequently falls to zero the residual magnetic flux density in the core is the remanence, B_m. A second pulse of current of magnitude I_m will switch conditions to those defined by point a and as the pulse decays to zero the operating point moves back to point b on the B axis. Note that there has been no change in the magnitude of B during this period. In practice, the line ab will not be horizontal, but the change in B will be small enough to be ignored. A current pulse of $-I_m$ will move the operating point to c, and back to b along the line cb; again there is no significant change in B.

The point of this exercise is to demonstrate that a current of magnitude I_m in either one, but not both, of the wires threading the core will not change the flux density in the core in any significant way once the core is saturated.

Now let us see what happens if we pass a current $-I_m$ simultaneously through both wires, assuming that the core has an initial flux density B_m. The operating point moves to d and as it does so there is a rapid change in flux density from plus to minus B_m. The flux in the core is thus reversed in a very decisive manner and removal of the current leaves the core in a magnetic state defined by point e. The core is thus made to behave as a two-state device. It is always in a state of magnetic saturation, but the direction of magnetisation can be clockwise or anticlockwise around the core. The core can therefore be used as a binary store with conditions at e representing zero and conditions at b representing plus one.

If we are to use this in an information system then we must be able to read the information that is contained in the core. Now the flux leakage from such a toroid is insignificant so that it will be very difficult to detect the state of magnetisation under steady state conditions. However, changes in flux within a magnetic circuit can be easily detected because if the circuit is surrounded by a conducting loop then a voltage is induced in that loop proportional to the rate of change of flux with time. What we do then is to set up the core in, say, the plus one state, and then pulse the two wires of figure 28.2 simultaneously with currents $-I_m$. As the flux in the core reverses we detect it by monitoring the voltage induced in a third wire which has been threaded through the core as in figure 28.3. If the core is initially in the zero state

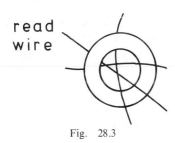

Fig. 28.3

then there is no flux change and no voltage induced in the read wire. In this way we can interrogate the core, but note that by giving the answer, the core loses its memory!

Now, why do we have two wires in figure 28.1 when one would do perfectly well?

The answer is only seen when we begin assembling a number of these cores to give us a large storage system. By using two wires we remove the need to allocate an individual wire to every core because we can use the two wires to thread a number of cores simultaneously. Figure 28.4 shows part of a typical pattern in a large matrix of cores. To magnetise the core at position $2B$ we send simultaneous current pulses of magnitude I_m along wire 2 and wire B. Only in core $2B$ is there sufficient magnetising force to saturate the core positively (assuming that all cores start in the zero state). All the other cores threaded by the '2' wire, and those threaded by the

'B' wire, effectively change conditions from points e to f and back to e, where these are as defined in figure 28.2.

28.3 MAGNETIC RECORDING

In sound recording a microphone is used to produce a time-varying electric current. The current is then passed through the magnetising winding of an electromagnet which establishes a time-varying magnetic field. A magnetic tape is passed through this field and the tape emerges with a permanent impression of the changing field pattern.

The magnet has a shape similar to that shown in figure 28.5. The airgap is fundamental to the recording process because it establishes the fringing field in which the tape is magnetised. The tape itself consists of a thin plastic backing with a fine layer of magnetic oxide particles on the surface. The particles act as small magnets with square loop characteristics so that they tend to change polarity only when the applied field exceeds a critical value. Before passing under the recording head the tape is demagnetised and any residual magnetism in the particles is randomly arranged to give no resultant effect. As the tape passes through the time-varying field of the recording head those particles that experience a field strength in excess of the critical value are magnetised in the direction of the field. The stronger the field, the greater is the number of particles magnetised so that the state of magnetisation of the surface layer of the tape is a record of the state of the field at the instant the tape passed under the recording head.

Detailed analysis of the recording process is extremely difficult because of the complexity of the leakage field. From the simple representation in figure 28.5 we can appreciate that the direction of the magnetic field strength vector varies from point to point across the tape and when the variation in the plane at right angles to the plane of the figure is allowed for, and the time variation of the signal, you can begin to see the enormous difficulties faced by anyone who tries to build an exact theoretical model. The tape itself is usually manufactured in such a way that the preferred direction of magnetisation lies in the plane of the tape. Its magnetic characteristics have features in common with those of bulk ferromagnetic materials and in particular the relationship between the exciting field and the induced magnetisation is not a linear one. The effect of this is illustrated very simply in figure 28.6. This shows how the non-linearity causes a sinusoidal input signal to be recorded as a distorted sine wave.

The solution to this problem of distortion is achieved by providing a high frequency a.c. biasing signal in the

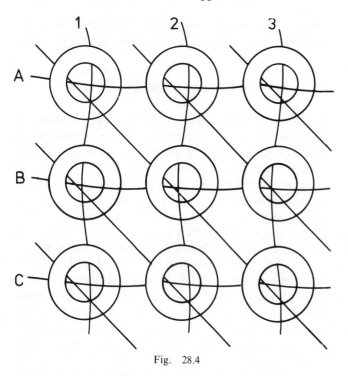

Fig. 28.4

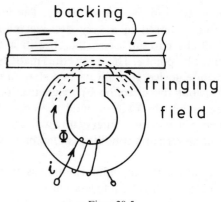

Fig. 28.5

coil of the recording magnet and then superimposing on this signal the time-varying input. The bias signal provides the energy to excite the magnetic particles and the input signal simply triggers some, or all of the particles into saturation. This improves the linearity of the recording process considerably.

The magnetic particles in the tape are of finite size and this gives rise to a statistical variation in the playback signal. The principle can be readily appreciated by considering an extreme case in which the tape has only a few, widely dispersed particles. The playback signal will then be a series of discrete pulses which occur as each particle moves under the playback head. A truly continuous signal cannot then be obtained from a magnetic tape, although a good approximation is achieved by using small densely packed and uniformly distributed particles in the magnetic layer. The order of particle density achieved in typical cases is 10^{12} particles per cubic millimetre.

Another source of noise is the playback head itself. This is a magnetic core which is very similar to the recording head shown in figure 28.5. The length of the

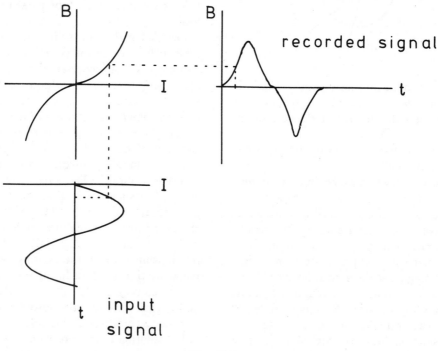

Fig. 28.6

airgap will be smaller in the playback head and usually less than the minimum recorded wavelength. As the magnetised tape passes over the recording head it will induce a time-varying signal in the coil which surrounds the magnetic core. It also produces time-varying currents in the conducting metal of the core itself and this can be a source of signal loss. To reduce this effect, the core is made of thin laminations which allow the magnetic flux to build up in the core as before, but which inhibit the circulation of the eddy currents in the plane at right angles to the flux flow. An alternative solution is to use a material which has a high electrical resistivity.

FURTHER READING

Tutorial Review of Magnetic Recording, J. S. Mallinson. *Proc. IEEE*, Vol. 64, No. 2, February 1976.

Magnetic Recording, V. E. Ragosine, *Scientific American*, Nov. 1969.

Task 14:   The Biot–Savart law

T14.1   INTRODUCTION

There are no new concepts to be learned in this Task. We have already developed the Biot-Savart equation in Task 9 and all we need now is some practice in its application. The law enables us to determine the magnetic flux density, or the magnetic field strength, at points around current-carrying conductors. It is more general in its application than the circuital law because, unlike the circuital law, it can be used to find both magnitude and direction of the magnetic field in any geometry.

T14.2   OBJECTIVES

When you have completed this Task you should be able to do the following:

(a) state the Biot-Savart in the form given in equation T14.1;
(b) explain in your own words, and to the satisfaction of a fellow student, the meaning of equation T14.1; and
(c) apply the law correctly to situations of the kind illustrated by the examples and problems in this Task.

T14.3   PRIOR WORK

It is important that you have read and understood Task 9 and in particular section T9.4.

T14.4   THE BIOT-SAVART LAW

The law is defined by the following equation:

$$\delta B_p = \frac{\mu_0 I \delta l \sin \beta}{4\pi r^2} \qquad \text{(T14.1)}$$

This defines the magnitude of the flux density component at a point p due to a current element $I\delta l$. The geometric relationship is shown in figure T14.1 and it is important

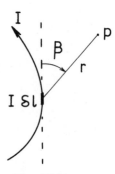

Fig.   T14.1

to remember that the line of action of δB is perpendicular to the plane which contains the element $I\delta l$ and the vector r. By adding together all the components δB at point p due to all the current elements $I\delta l$ we can obtain the resultant flux density at p due to the current circuit. The summation may well be complicated because B is a vector quantity and the various elements δB_p may well be in different directions. The following common example demonstrates the use of the law in a case in which the elements δB_p are all in the same sense at any one point in space.

T14.5   THE MAGNETIC FLUX DENSITY PRODUCED BY A LONG, STRAIGHT, CURRENT-CARRYING CONDUCTOR

The problem is illustrated in figure T14.2 which shows a conductor of length L carrying a current I. We wish to calculate the flux density at point p due to the current.

The contribution to the flux density at p made by the elemental current length $I\delta l$ is given by:

$$\delta B_p = \frac{\mu_0 \sin \beta}{4\pi r^2} I\delta l \qquad \text{(T14.2)}$$

This component is directed into the plane of the paper in figure T14.2 and it will be seen that all other components due to all other current elements are in the same direction so that in this case the summation of the elements δB_p is an algebraic sum. Before we can carry out this summation by integration we must write the

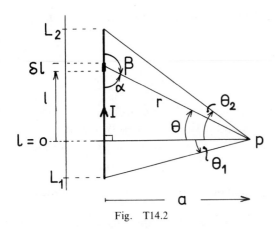

Fig. T14.2

T14.6 THE MAGNETIC FLUX DENSITY ON THE AXIS OF A CIRCULAR LOOP CARRYING CURRENT

In this example we shall find that the elements δB_p at a point lie in different directions and the summation then has to allow for this. The problem is illustrated in figure T14.3. The component of flux density δB_p due to

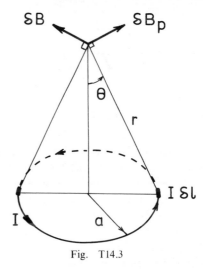

Fig. T14.3

variables r and β of equation T14.2 in terms of the length l.

$$\sin \beta = \sin \alpha = \frac{a}{r} \quad \text{and} \quad r^2 = a^2 + l^2$$

so that

$$\delta B_p = \frac{\mu_0 a}{4\pi (a^2 + l^2)^{3/2}} I\delta l \qquad \text{(T14.3)}$$

To obtain B_p we sum equation T14.3 as δl varies from $-L_1$ to L_2. Thus

$$B_p = \int_{-L_1}^{L_2} \frac{\mu_0 a I}{4\pi (a^2 + l^2)^{3/2}} \, dl \qquad \text{(T14.4)}$$

This integration is solved by substitution, as follows:

let $l = a \tan \theta$, then $dl = a \sec^2 \theta \, d\theta$ and the limits of integration $-L_1$ and L_2 become $-\theta_1$ and θ_2 respectively. We can also show that

$$\frac{a^3}{(a^2 + l^2)^{3/2}} = \cos^3 \theta$$

and substitution of these values into equation T14.4 gives

$$B_p = \frac{\mu_0 I}{4\pi a} \int_{-\theta_1}^{\theta_2} \cos \theta \, d\theta$$

$$\therefore \ B_p = \frac{\mu_0 I}{4\pi a} (\sin \theta_2 + \sin \theta_1) \qquad \text{(T14.5)}$$

If we consider a conductor of infinite length, then both θ_1 and θ_2 tend to $\pi/2$ and equation T14.5 tends to:

$$B_p = \frac{\mu_0 I}{2\pi a}$$

For the particular case of the infinitely long, straight conductor, the solution for B_p is more easily obtained by using the circuital law.

the current element $I\delta l$ acts at a right angle to the plane containing the line r and the vector $I\delta l$. Diammetrically opposite to $I\delta l$ in the ring there will be another, identical current element which will produce a component δB at point p. From the symmetry of the situation we can see that the horizontal component of these two flux density vectors will cancel and we can deduce that in fact there will be no horizontal resultant of flux density at any point on the axis through the centre of the ring.

The vertical component of δB_p is $\delta B_p \sin \theta$. Using the Biot–Savart law we have:

$$\delta B_p = \frac{\mu_0 I\delta l}{4\pi r^2}$$

since $\beta = 90^p$, and therefore the resultant flux density along the vertical axis is

$$B = \int_0^{2\pi a} \frac{\mu_0 I \sin \theta \, dl}{4\pi r^2} = \mu_0 I \sin \theta \frac{a}{2r^2}$$

Since $\sin \theta = a/r$, we can write

$$B = \mu_0 I \frac{a^2}{2r^3}$$

T14.7 THE FLUX DENSITY ALONG THE AXIS OF A SOLENOID

This is another common example which can be found

in several textbooks—so why repeat it here? Simply because most texts treat it as a mathematical exercise and omit the interesting bit. This is to be found at the beginning of the solution with the identification of the real problem and the development of a plan for its solution. Take an extreme case with a couple of turns of wire wound onto a long, cylindrical former as shown in figure T14.4.

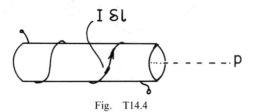

Fig. T14.4

We know that we can write down the value of flux density at the point p due to the element of current $I\delta l$, but in which sense is it acting? And when we add up all the contributions from all the elements $I\delta l$ in the coil how do we allow for the twist and turn of the $I\delta l$ vector as it goes around the core? No doubt with time, care and a lot of help we could sort it out, but in the meantime what about the solenoid in which the turns are closely packed. There is still a spiral effect though it is not as marked as in figure T14.4. If we could really pack the turns so tightly that there was no space between them, then the effect of the spiral would disappear. So, we have identified one problem and can overcome it if the solenoid is tightly wound. The next problem is to calculate the flux density along the axis of this tightly wound solenoid and this again is solved by imaginative thinking. Imagine that the N turns make contact with each other so that they form an effective sheet of conducting material around the circumference of the former, as in figure T14.5. The total current in this sheet is IN where I is the current in each of the N turns. Can we break up this cylinder of current into elemental rings?

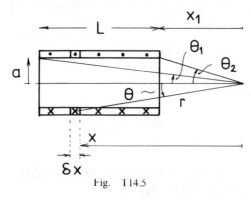

Fig. T14.5

Let one such ring have a width δx. The current in the ring is $(IN/L)\delta x$ and we can solve for the flux density at p

due to this current using the method of the previous section.

Thus

$$B_p = \mu_0 \frac{a^2}{2r^3} \frac{IN}{L} \delta x$$

Adding all the contributions from all the rings of width δx we obtain the total flux density at p as

$$B = \mu_0 \frac{IN}{L} \int_{x_1}^{x_1 + L} \frac{a^2}{2r^3} dx$$

The solution of the integral by substitution then follows:

$$x = \frac{a}{\tan \theta} \quad \text{and} \quad dx = \frac{-a \, d\theta}{\sin^2 \theta}$$

also $\sin \theta = a/r$, so that the integral becomes

$$-\int_{\theta_2}^{\theta_1} \frac{\sin \theta}{2} d\theta = \frac{1}{2} (\cos \theta_1 - \cos \theta_2)$$

$$\therefore B = \mu_0 \frac{IN}{2L} (\cos \theta_1 - \cos \theta_2) \qquad \text{(T14.6)}$$

T14.8 SELF-ASSESSMENT QUESTIONS

Question 1

The Biot–Savart law is written as

$$\delta B_p = \frac{\mu_0 I \delta l \sin \beta}{4\pi r^2}$$

In which of the diagrams of figure T14.6 are both β and r defined correctly?

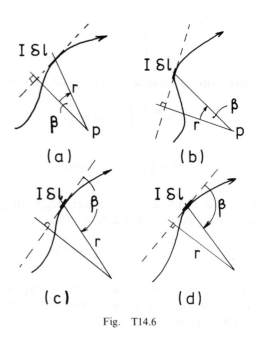

Fig. T14.6

Question 2

Derive an expression for the magnetic flux density at the centre of a square loop of wire of side d, carrying a current I.

Question 3

One current-carrying busbar passes over another in the manner shown in figure T14.7. Determine the magnitude and direction of the magnetic field strength due to I at the point p, where the second busbar crosses the plane of the loop $abcd$. The dimensions of the loop are as follows:

$$ab = cd = 4 \text{ cm}; \; bc = 6 \text{ cm}; \text{ and } ap = pd$$

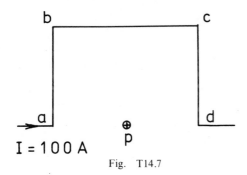

Fig. T14.7

Question 4

A conductor is bent into a plane semi-circle of radius 0.5 m. A current of 100 A flows in the conductor. Using the Biot–Savart law, find the resultant magnetic field strength at a point on the axis of the semi-circle distance 0.5 m from the centre of the semi-circle due to the current in the semi-circle.

Question 5

A solenoid of length 25 cm with a circular cross-section of radius 5 cm is uniform wound with 250 turns of wire. Determine the flux density at the centre point of the solenoid and at a point on the axis distance 25 cm from the centre when a current of 1 A exists in the winding.

T14.9 ANSWERS AND SOLUTIONS

1. Figure T14.6c

2. Consider one side of length d, carrying a current I. The centre of the coil is a perpendicular distance $d/2$ away from the mid-point of the side. Using equation T14.5 we obtain.

$$B = \frac{\mu_0 I}{2\pi d} 2 \sin 45^\circ = \frac{\mu_0 I}{\sqrt{2}\pi d}$$

The other three sides contribute a flux density of the same magnitude and in the same direction. Thus the total flux density is $4\mu_0 I/\sqrt{2}\pi d$.

3. Using equation T14.5 to obtain H_p,

H_p due to I in side $ab = 212$ Am^{-1}
H_p due to I in side $cd = 212$ Am^{-1}
H_p due to I in side $bc = 239$ Am^{-1}

All three vectors have the same direction at point p so that the total at p is 663 Am^{-1}.

4. In figure T14.8,

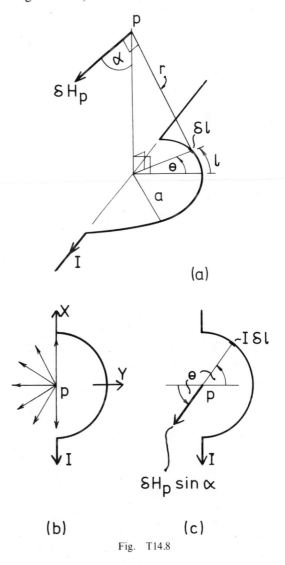

(a)

(b)　　　　(c)

Fig. T14.8

$$\delta H_p = \frac{I\delta l}{4\pi r^2}$$

The vertical component is $\delta H_p \cos \alpha$, and the sum of all vertical components gives $H_z = 17.7 \ \text{Am}^{-1}$.

The horizontal components of δH_p themselves have components which can be resolved in directions parallel to and perpendicular to the diameter joining the open ends of the semi-circle. Denoting these directions x and y as in figure T14.8 we can see that the resultant in the x direction will be zero. In the y direction, $\delta H_y = \delta H_p \sin \alpha \cos \theta$ but, $l = a\theta$ so that $\delta l = a\delta\theta$ and

$$\delta H_y = \frac{I}{4\pi r^2} a \sin \alpha \cos \theta \ \delta\theta.$$

To obtain the total component H_y this expression is integrated as θ varies from $-\pi/2$ to $\pi/2$.

$$H_y = \frac{Ia}{2\pi r^2}\sin \alpha = 11.3 \ \text{Am}^{-1}$$

The resultant magnitude of H is 21 Am^{-1} and it acts in the yz plane making an angle 58° to the horizontal.

5. Substitution of values into equation T14.6 gives

   (a) $B = 1.2 \ 10^{-3}$ T
   (b) $B = 40 \ 10^{-6}$ T

CHAPTER 30

Task 15: Electromagnetic induction

T15.1 INTRODUCTION

Faraday's law of electromagnetic induction is one of the first laws of electromagnetism and the effect which it describes is of fundamental importance. Electromagnetic machines and transformers operate as they do only because there is an induction effect. Nor is the effect confined to machines. In electric circuits generally the phenomenon we know as *inductance* is but another aspect of electromagnetic induction.

In developing an extension to Ampère's law in Chapter 24 we saw that a changing electric field gave rise to a magnetic field. Faraday's law gives us the rest of the picture and shows how a changing magnetic field gives rise to an electric field.

T15.2 OBJECTIVES

When you have completed this unit you should be able to do the following:

(a) state Faraday's law;
(b) define correctly the magnitude and sense of the e.m.f. induced in a coil by a changing flux-linkage;
(c) distinguish between motional e.m.f. and transformer e.m.f.; and
(d) calculate the e.m.f. induced around closed loops and between points on a conductor due to change of flux with time and due to motion of conductors.

T15.3 PRIOR KNOWLEDGE

A knowledge of Tasks 8 and 9 will be helpful, particularly in section T15.5.

T15.4 ELECTROMAGNETIC INDUCTION

It would be possible to predict some features of this phenomenon from the work we have already done, but let us begin, as Faraday did, with an experimental observation. Let us take a conducting loop and position it in a magnetic flux Φ, as illustrated in figure T15.1a. If the flux through the loop is changed by an amount $\Delta\Phi$ in a time Δt there is a current induced around the loop. If $\Delta\Phi$ adds to Φ then the current induced is in the sense shown in figure T15.1b. The flow of current is in such a sense that the magnetic field it produces tends to oppose the change in field which caused the induction. All this can be demonstrated with equipment which is available in any electrical science laboratory.

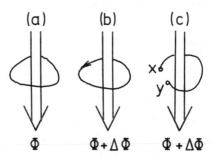

Fig. T15.1

Let us now break the loop of figure T15.1c and continue to increase the flux Φ. A potential difference will be measured between points X and Y, either side of the break.

Question 1

Which point has the higher electric potential, X or Y?

The equivalent circuit shown in the answer defines the potential difference as V. If points X and Y are connected, then a current will flow from X through the connections to Y. The magnitude of the potential difference is proportional to the rate of change of flux linking the loop and when V is defined as above

$$V = \frac{d\Phi}{dt} \qquad (T15.1)$$

This is Faraday's law.

This statement covers two quite distinct effects because the rate of change of flux through the loop can be obtained in different ways. Perhaps the most obvious way is to change the magnitude of the flux with time. This we can do by moving the source of magnetism relative to the loop or by varying the current which produces the field. The first we can demonstrate by passing a bar magnet through a loop and the second is the well known transformer effect. In both cases we consider the loop to be stationary and we change the flux through the loop.

The alternative method of induction is to keep the field constant and move the loop across the field so that the flux through the loop varies with time. In both examples Faraday's law holds, but the cause of the potential difference is attributed to different mechanisms.

We could write the law as follows:

$$V = \left(\frac{d\Phi}{dt}\right)_{\substack{\text{for varying} \\ \text{field}}} + \left(\frac{d\Phi}{dt}\right)_{\substack{\text{due to} \\ \text{motion}}} \qquad (T15.2)$$

T15.5 THE FLUX-CUTTING RULE

The second term in the above equation is often referred to as the flux-cutting rule. This in fact is the part of the law which we could have predicted. If we go back to section T9.4 and equation T9.5 we can see that we defined the force on a charge Q_2 moving with velocity u_2 as

$$F = Q_2 u_2 \frac{K Q_1 u_1 \sin \beta}{r^2} = Q_2 u_2 B$$

The force per unit charge is $u_2 B$ and by definition this is the electric field strength at the point occupied by Q_2. Any charge moving through that point with velocity u_2 experiences an electric field strength $u_2 B$ and a force $Q u_2 B$.

Let us establish a uniform magnetic field of flux density B and move a conductor across the field with a velocity u as in figure T15.2. All the free charge in the conductor experiences an electric field uB and the free charges separate, as shown in the diagram, until the

electrostatic field produced by the charge separation equals the force developed by movement in the magnetic field. The potential difference of X with respect to Y is

$$V_{XY} = -\int_Y^X E \, dx = \int_Y^X uB \, dx$$

since E is equal and opposite to uB.
Hence,

$$V_{XY} = uBl$$

where l is the length of the conductor. uBl is described as the electromotive force, or e.m.f., a term which is well established but misleading. The units of e.m.f. are Joules/Coulomb or Volts.

We can now extend our experiment as follows. The conductor XY is allowed to roll along two conducting rails and a third conductor ST completes a conducting loop. As the bar XY is pushed to the right in figure T15.3 the e.m.f. induced in XY causes a current flow around the loop $XSTY$: as XY moves through a distance δx the area of the loop increases by $l\delta x$ and the increase in flux through the loop is $Bl\delta x$. At a velocity u it takes a time $\delta t = \delta x / u$ to move δx. Using Faraday's law for the e.m.f. induced around the loop,

$$V = \frac{d\Phi}{dt} = \frac{Bl\delta x}{\delta t} = Blu$$

So we see that when a conducting loop moves across a magnetic field we can explain the induction of voltage either as a flux-cutting effect or as the result of a change in flux linking. What we cannot do is to determine the potential V_{XY} in figure T15.2 by Faraday's law, because the law applies to closed contours or closed loops.

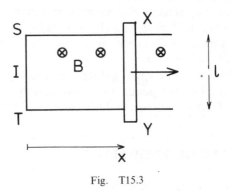

Fig. T15.3

T15.6 SELF-ASSESSMENT QUESTIONS

Question 2

A vehicle has a straight vertical radio aerial 2 m long mounted on its roof. The vehicle travels at 60 m.p.h. along a road parallel to an overhead transmission line so

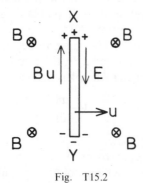

Fig. T15.2

that the aerial is vertically below the line conductor. The conductor carries a direct current of 200 A and the direction of positive current flow is the same as the direction of motion of the car. Determine the e.m.f. induced in the aerial if the top of the aerial is 6 m below the line. Which end of the aerial is positive?

Question 3

A long straight lightning conductor lies in the same plane as a rectangular metal window frame. The window has sides of length 1 m and 1.5 m. The shorter sides are parallel to the lightning conductor and the nearer side is 0.5 m from it.

If the current in the lightning conductor rises from zero at a constant rate of 3×10^{10} A s^{-1}, determine the e.m.f. induced around the metal window frame.

Question 4

A conducting circular disc of area A spins on an axis through its centre at a constant N revolutions per second. The plane of the disc is at right angles to a uniform and constant magnetic flux density B. Two sliding electrical contacts are made to the disc, one at the centre and one at the rim.

Show that the e.m.f. induced between these contacts by the rotation of the disc in the field is given by:

$$V = BNA$$

If the flux density across the disc is now made non-uniform so that B at any radius r from the axis is given by $B_r = 0.1\,r$, determine the resultant e.m.f. induced between the two contacts on a 10 cm radius disc rotating at 15 r.p.s.

Question 5

(a) A large horizontal flat winding represented by MM' in figure T15.4a is supplied with direct current. This produces a magnetic field which acts in a direction perpendicular to the plane of the winding and which is uniform through space. A rectangular, single-turn, coil CC' is fixed above the winding and can be moved to left or right along a line parallel to the plane.

Describe briefly the electrical conditions that exist in the rectangular coil in each of the following cases:

  (i) coil CC' fixed and main winding moving to the left with constant velocity u;
  (ii) main winding fixed and coil moving to the right with velocity u;

(b) the main winding is now reconnected so that it gives a flux density distribution along the x axis as shown in figure T15.4b. The rectangular coil is moved in the direction of increasing x with a constant velocity of 10 m s^{-1}. The length of each coil side is 0.1 m.

Determine the magnitude and sense of the resultant e.m.f. induced around the coil as it moves from $x = 0$ to $x = 1.0$ m.

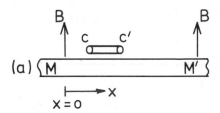

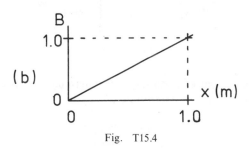

Fig. T15.4

Question 6

A rectangular coil with sides of length a and b has N turns and spins with uniform angular velocity ω about an axis which is parallel to the a sides and which passes through the mid-points of the b sides. The coil spins in a uniform field of flux density B which acts perpendicular to a plane through the axis of rotation. Obtain an expression for the e.m.f. induced around the coil.

Question 7

Referring back to Question 5, if the coil CC' were rigidly fixed to the main winding would there be an e.m.f. induced in any part of the coil,

  (a) when the main winding was stationary, and,
  (b) when the main winding moved?

T15.7 ANSWERS AND SOLUTIONS

1. X (see figure T15.5)

2. Treating the overhead line as a long conductor and

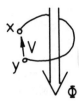

Fig. T15.5

ignoring the effects of earth, the flux density at a point distance x from the conductor is:

$$B_x = \frac{\mu_0 I}{2\pi x} \quad \text{(see figure T15.6)}$$

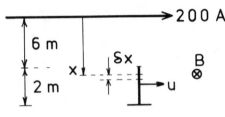

Fig. T15.6

The element of aerial at x, of length δx has an e.m.f. induced in it of magnitude

$$\delta V = Blu = \frac{\mu_0 I}{2\pi x} u \delta x$$

The total e.m.f. in the aerial is,

$$V = \int_{x=6}^{x=8} \frac{\mu_0 I}{2\pi x} u \, dx = \frac{\mu_0 I u}{2\pi} \ln\left(\frac{8}{6}\right) = 3.10^{-4} \text{ V}$$

The top of the aerial is positive with respect to the bottom.

3. This is clearly a case of a transformer e.m.f. The flux passing through the window at any instant can be found by the method used in solution 3 in Task 11.

$$\Phi = \frac{\mu_0 I}{2\pi} \ln 4$$

When $I = 3 \, 10^{10} \, t$ A,

$$\Phi = \frac{\mu_0 \ln 4}{2\pi} 3 \, 10^{10} \, t$$

and

$$V = \frac{d\Phi}{dt} = 8.3 \text{ kV}$$

4. This is an example of flux cutting.
We take an elemental strip at radius r of thickness δr, as shown in figure T15.7 and determine the e.m.f. across it.

$$\delta V = Blu = B_r \omega r \delta r$$

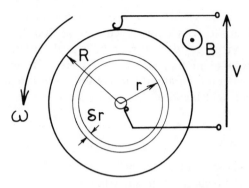

Fig. T15.7

$$\therefore V = B\omega \int_0^R r \, dr = B\omega \frac{R^2}{2} = ABN$$

If $B = 0.1 \, r$, then $\delta V = 0.1 \omega r^2 \, \delta r$

and

$$V = 0.1\omega \int_0^R r^2 \, dr = 0.1\omega \frac{R^3}{3} = 3.14 \text{ mV}$$

5. (a) (i) With the coil CC' fixed there can be no motional e.m.f. induced around the coil. Only the transformer e.m.f. is possible and if we look carefully at the case we see that this is zero. There is no change of flux through the coil, provided that the flux density remains constant everywhere. In electrical terms, the coil CC' is unaware of the movement of the stator.

(ii) The transformer e.m.f. is again zero because there is no change in flux linking the coil. The motional e.m.f. about the coil is also zero because $d\Phi/dt$ is zero, but if we examine the case more closely we discover that e.m.f.s are induced in the sides of CC' which are at right angles to x. These are equal in magnitude and sense and the resultant around the loop is zero.

(b)
$$V = \frac{d\Phi}{dt} = 0.01 \frac{dB}{dt}$$

but

$$B = kx$$

where

$$k = 1.0 \text{ T m}^{-1}$$

$$\frac{dB}{dt} = \frac{dx}{dt} = u$$

$$\therefore V = 0.01 \times 10 = 0.1 \text{ volts}$$

6. A section through the coil is shown in figure T15.8.

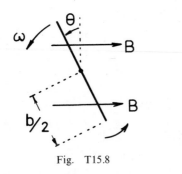

Fig. T15.8

The flux passing through the coil in the position shown is given by:

$$\Phi = BA \cos \theta = BA \cos \omega t$$

$$\frac{d\Phi}{dt} = -BA\omega \sin \omega t$$

The e.m.f. induced in the N loops of the coil is $-NBA\omega \sin \omega t$ where $A = ab$.

7. (a) In this case there is clearly no change in flux through the coil and no motion of the coil with respect to the field. $V = 0$.

(b) There is no transformer e.m.f. induced because the field produced by the stator is uniform and static, even though the stator is moving, but e.m.f.s are induced in the sides of the coil which are at right angles to x. Summing around the loop, the resultant e.m.f. is zero because the effects in the two sides are equal in magnitude and opposite in sense.

CHAPTER 31

The new ice age

31.1 INTRODUCTION

In the Leiden Physics Laboratory in 1908, helium was liquefied for the first time. Three years later, in the same laboratories, a series of experiments was carried out to investigate the electrical conductivities of metals at temperatures near that of liquid helium (about 4 K). A mercury wire was found to have a very low resistance above 4 K, as indeed was predicted, but at about 4 K the resistance suddenly collapsed to such a low value that it could not be measured. Subsequent investigations have shown that many other metals and alloys behave in the same way at very low temperatures. This state of zero resistance is known as superconductivity.

For many years the impact of this discovery on electrical technology was insignificant, but with the growth of semiconductor technology and the start of the space race interest in low temperature physics grew and the possibility of applying superconductivity to practical systems was examined anew.

31.2 SUPERCONDUCTORS

Early superconducting materials were limited to operation in magnetic flux densities less than one tesla because in stronger fields the conductors switched back to the normal resistive state. A similar effect occurred at high current densities. Both effects were the result of the penetration of the superconductor by the magnetic flux. At low fields and low currents the depth of penetration is small, but it increases with increasing flux or current until a critical value is reached. Later developments led to conductors which could operate in much higher fields, but satisfactory operation at high current densities was not achieved until a new form of conductor was developed in the 1960s. The problem was that a fluctuation in the field conditions about a conductor carrying a large current could cause one small section of the conductor to go resistive. As soon as this happened a power loss occurred which caused local heating and adjacent sections of conductor would then go resistive.

This led to normalisation of the whole conductor.

The solution to the problem was to encase the superconductor in copper so that when one section went resistive the current would divert into the copper sheath and so bypass the unstable section. The copper loss would be much less than the loss in the normalised superconductor so that the associated temperature rise could be kept below the critical value.

31.3 APPLICATIONS

The development of the new types of superconductor came with the development of large supercooled magnets. There was a need in high-energy physics for magnets which could produce fields of 5 T and upwards for bending and focusing in particle accelerators. There were also anticipated needs for larger magnets to contain the plasma in the controlled thermonuclear fusion reactors that were being planned. Superconducting magnets were attractive because of the large current densities that could be produced in resistance-free conductors.

This same feature attracts the electrical engineer because the high currents and flux densities in a superconducting field winding promise savings in weight, size and cost. Designs for large superconducting generators are being carefully studied and superconducting motors have been built. The very first was a 2.7 MW (3550 h.p.) machine built by the International Research and Development Co Ltd, at Newcastle upon Tyne. The savings in weight and size make superconducting motors an attractive proposition for ship propulsion. Until now the advantages of electric propulsion have always been overshadowed by its comparative size and weight. One interesting outcome of these developments has been the re-appraisal of the homopolar machine. This is basically the Faraday disc that we met in Task 14, question 4, and it can be worked as a generator or as a motor. As a generator it produces a direct current without the need for commutators, but it is inherently a low voltage machine.

31.4 A SUPERCONDUCTING HOMOPOLAR MACHINE

The Faraday disc is a very simple homopolar generator and consists of a conducting disc which is rotated about an axis through its centre, perpendicular to the plane of the disc. A steady magnetic field is maintained across the plane of the disc, as illustrated in figure 31.1, and the output voltage is generated between the axis and the disc rim. At constant speed the machine produces a steady output voltage and the output current is only limited by the resistance in the circuit.

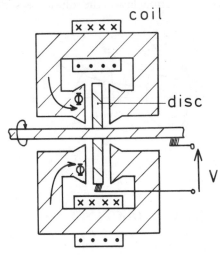

Fig. 31.1

The machine has two useful features: it does not require a commutator and the load current in the disc does not produce a demagnetising field. It has particular disadvantages in that it is a d.c. generator—and there are clear advantages in using a.c. for power transmission and distribution—and it is a low voltage machine. We showed in Task 15 that the output voltage of such a machine is given by $V = ABN$ where A is the disc area, B the flux density of the exciting field and N the number of revolutions per second. There is a limit to the speed at which one can rotate a disc of given area, which is determined largely by the strength of the disc material, so that increased output voltage depends on our ability to increase the flux density of the field.

A superconducting field coil does not use iron and can produce field strengths significantly larger than those found in normal electric machines. This gives a double advantage of increased output voltage and reduced weight. Further increases in voltage can be achieved by using a segmented disc, or multiple discs, and connecting the elements in series.

Motor operation is achieved by connecting a d.c. source between the sliding contacts on the axis and the rim of the disc. This is basically how the IRDC machine worked and it developed 2.7 MW at 200 r.p.m.

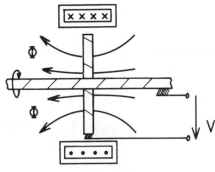

Fig. 31.2

Whether motoring or generating, the current in the rotor has to pass through sliding contacts and this can cause problems. Typical carbon brushes used for current collection in standard machines operate at current densities between 15 and 25 A cm^{-2}, but it has been estimated that to take full advantage of superconducting homopolar generators current densities in the brushes may have to be as high as 350 A cm^{-2}. This is a very considerable increase and a great deal of development work is still needed. One possibility is to use a liquid metal connection between the moving and the stationary contacts. The high current densities might then be achieved, but unfortunately the available metals are likely to cause secondary problems as for example the health hazard of mercury vapour.

31.5 MAGNETIC LEVITATION OF VEHICLES

Proposals have been made for levitation systems using superconducting magnets on high speed trains. Essentially, the idea is to mount the magnets on the vehicle above a track system containing short-circuited conducting coils. As the train passes over the coils there will be a current induced in them because of the time-varying flux linkage through the coils. The currents in the coils will repel the circulating currents in the super-conducting magnets and provided that this lift can be transferred to the main structure of the vehicle it is theoretically possible to obtain levitation of the train. Unfortunately the train will still need wheels for low speed operation since the lift is a function of speed. There is also the problem of transferring the lifting force from the magnet system, which is supercooled, to the vehicle structure, which is at ambient temperature. Here again the advantages of supercooling are increased current and field strength with decreased weight because of the absence of magnetic steel.

FURTHER READING

Superconducting Electrical Machinery, C. J. Mole *et al.*, *Proc. IEEE*, Vol. 61, No. 1, January 1973.

CHAPTER 32

Task 16: Mutual and self inductance

T16.1 INTRODUCTION

You have probably already met with the concept of inductance as a parameter in electric circuit theory. The e.m.f. in an electric circuit invariably includes a component which is proportional to the rate of change of current in the circuit with time. The constant of proportionality is defined as the self-inductance. The effect we see is however just another aspect of Faraday's law and since this is the case it follows that inductance is better defined in terms of electromagnetic induction. Once this definition is made we can produce an algorithm for predicting the self-inductance of common arrangements of conductors.

Mutual inductance can also be defined either in terms of circuit theory or field theory and again there is an easy algorithm for the calculation of this quantity.

T16.2 OBJECTIVES

When you have finished this Task you should be able to:

(a) define the mutual inductance between two circuits as the flux linkages of one circuit caused by unit current in the other circuit;
(b) define the mutual inductance between two circuits as the e.m.f. induced in one by a unit rate of change of current with time in the other;
(c) define self-inductance in terms of the flux linkages of a circuit and the current in that circuit causing the flux linkage;
(d) define self-inductance in terms of the e.m.f. induced in a circuit by a unit rate of change of current with time in that circuit; and
(e) calculate self and mutual inductances of simple circuits of the kind illustrated in the self-assessment questions.

T16.3 PRIOR WORK

This Task follows on naturally from what has gone

before and you should be familiar with this. You will need to use the circuital law in the solution of some of the questions.

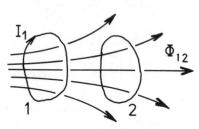

Fig. T16.1

T16.4 MUTUAL INDUCTANCE

In the arrangement shown in figure T16.1, part of the flux produced by the current I_1 in loop 1 passes across the surface bounded by loop 2. We denote this flux Φ_{12} and if the flux is time-varying then an e.m.f. V_2 is induced in coil 2 with a magnitude

$$V_2 = \frac{d\Phi_{12}}{dt}$$

If the second coil has N_2 turns then

$$V_2 = N_2 \frac{d\Phi_{12}}{dt}$$

Now the flux density at each and every point on the surface area of coil 2 is directly proportional to I_1, provided that the intervening medium has a linear magnetisation characteristic. This follows from the Biot–Savart law. We can therefore write

$$N_2 \Phi_{12} \propto I_1$$

or

$$N_2 \Phi_{12} = M_{12} I_1 \qquad \text{(T16.1)}$$

where M_{12} is a constant known as the mutual inductance of circuit 2 with circuit 1.

$$V_2 = N_2 \frac{d\Phi_{12}}{dt} = M_{12} \frac{dI_1}{dt} \qquad \text{(T16.2)}$$

The product $N_2\Phi_{12}$ is referred to as the flux linkages of circuit 2 due to the current I_1. If we use the symbol λ for flux linkages, we can write

$$M_{12} = \frac{\lambda_{12}}{I_1} \qquad (T16.3)$$

Equations T16.2 and T16.3 provide us with the alternative definitions of mutual inductance.

The procedure for calculating mutual inductance is clear and straightforward.

We assume a current I_1 in circuit 1;
we determine the flux linking circuit 2 due to the current I_1;
we calculate the flux linkages, λ_{12}; and
we calculate the mutual inductance using equation T16.3.

The units of mutual inductance are the same as the units of self-inductance—the Henry (H). The following example will illustrate the method and lead us to a further discovery.

Let the mean circumference of the steel ring in figure T16.2 be l, let the cross-sectional area be A and let the windings 1 and 2 carry currents I_1 and I_2 through turns N_1 and N_2 respectively. Assume that the steel is being worked on a linear portion of its magnetisation characteristic at a point where the relative permeability is μ_r.

To find M_{12}

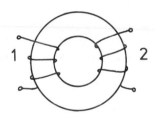

Fig. T16.2

Assume a steady current I_1 in coil 1. This establishes a magnetic field strength H in the core which is determined by the circuital law as

$$H = \frac{N_1 I_1}{l}$$

The flux in the core due to I_1 is then

$$\Phi_1 = \mu_0 \mu_r \frac{A N_1 I_1}{l} \qquad (T16.4)$$

If there is no leakage, then

$$\Phi_{12} = \Phi_1$$

therefore

$$\lambda_{12} = \mu_0 \mu_r \frac{A N_1 N_2 I_1}{l}$$

and

$$M_{12} = \mu_0 \mu_r \frac{A N_1 N_2}{l}$$

Now, following exactly the same procedure, show for yourself that the mutual inductance of circuit 1 with circuit 2 is given by:

$$M_{21} = \mu_0 \mu_r \frac{A N_1 N_2}{l}$$

The fact that $M_{12} = M_{21}$ is not a fortunate result of the symmetry of this magnetic circuit, it is true in all cases. If two electric circuits can be coupled by a mutual flux then the mutual inductance of one with respect to the other is the same as the mutual inductance of the other with respect to the one.

T16.5 SELF INDUCTANCE

Let us allow the current I_1 in figure T16.2 to vary with time. We can see from equation T16.4 that the flux in the core is proportional to I_1 and the flux linkages of coil 1 caused by the current I_1 can be written as:

$$\lambda_1 = N_1 \Phi_1 \propto I_1$$

We define the constant of proportionality as the self inductance of coil 1, L_1, so that

$$\lambda_1 = N_1 \Phi_1 = L_1 I_1 \qquad (T16.5)$$

There is an e.m.f. V_1 induced around the turns of coil 1 by the changing flux linkage, and

$$V_1 = N_1 \frac{d\Phi_1}{dt} = \frac{d\lambda_1}{dt} = L_1 \frac{dI_1}{dt} \qquad (T16.6)$$

Equations T16.5 and T16.6 provide the alternative definitions of self inductance. To determine self inductance we proceed as follows:

we assume a current I in the circuit in question;
we determine the flux linking the coil due to the current in the coil;
we calculate the flux linkages λ; and
we calculate the self inductance using equation T16.5.

To find L_1 for figure T16.2

Assume a current I_1 in coil 1. The flux through coil is given by equation T16.4, and the flux linkages λ_1 are therefore:

$$\lambda_1 = \mu_0 \mu_r \frac{A N_1^2}{l} I_1$$

and

$$L_1 = \mu_0 \mu_r \frac{A N_1^2}{l}$$

Now, following the same procedure, obtain an expression for the self inductance L_2 of coil 2. The answer should be obvious and if it is you should still check through the procedure because it is the method we need to know, not the answer.

If we multiply L_1 by L_2 and take the square root we can show that

$$M = \sqrt{L_1 L_2}$$

Now, this is a special case—special because all the flux produced by coil 1 passes through coil 2. In the more general case represented by figure T16.1 only a fraction of the flux produced by loop 1 passes through loop 2 and the relationship between the mutual and self inductances is given by

$$M = k\sqrt{L_1 L_2}$$

where the constant k is known as the coefficient of coupling.

T16.6   SELF-ASSESSMENT QUESTIONS

Question 1

A steel ring of 20 cm mean diameter and 12 cm^2 cross-sectional area is wound with two coils each with 200 turns. Determine the self and mutual inductances of the coils if the relative permeability of the steel is constant at 1000.

Question 2

A long coaxial cylindrical cable has an inner conductor of diameter d and an outer conductor of diameter D. Show that the self inductance per metre length of the cable is given by:

$$L = \frac{\mu_0}{2\pi} \ln (D/d)$$

Question 3

Two long, straight, cylindrical conductors each of radius r are separated by a distance d. The conductors are used as a go-and-return circuit. Show that the loop inductance per unit length is:

$$L = \frac{\mu_0}{2\pi} \ln \left(\frac{d-r}{r} \right)$$

Question 4

Four long straight conductors lie in the same horizontal plane with 1 cm between adjacent conductors. The two left-hand conductors supply a circuit with 500 mA r.m.s. current at 12.5 kHz. Determine the e.m.f. per metre run induced around the loop formed by the two right-hand conductors and the mutual inductance between the two loops per unit length.

Question 5

A toroid of 5 cm mean diameter has a cross-sectional area of 2 cm^2 and a radial airgap of 5 mm long. A coil of 200 turns is wound on the toroid. Determine the self-inductance of the coil. Assume that the relative permeability of the core material is 1000.

Question 6

Two coils are coupled magnetically and have a mutual inductance of 0.3 H. The current in one coil increases at a rate of 10 A s^{-1}. Determine the e.m.f. induced around the second loop during this period.

Question 7

Two coils, A and B, are so positioned that 60 per cent of the magnetic flux produced by A passes through the coil B. A current of 6 A in coil A produces a total flux of 1.8 m Wb. If coil B has 1500 turns determine

(a) the mutual inductance between the coils, and
(b) the e.m.f. induced around B when the current of 6 A in A is reduced linearly to zero in 1 ms.

Question 8

A long, straight lightning conductor lies in the same plane as a rectangular metal window frame. The window has sides of length 1 m and 1.5 m. The shorter sides are parallel to the lightning conductor and the nearer side is 0.5 m from it. Determine the mutual inductance between the two circuits.

Question 9

Figure T16.3 shows two mutually coupled coils with self inductances L_1 and L_2 and a mutual inductance M. In figure T16.3a they are connected in series aiding and in figure T16.3b they are in series opposition.

(a) Indicate on the diagrams the positive sense of the e.m.f.s induced by the current flow shown.
(b) Write down expressions for V in terms of L_1, L_2, M and I.

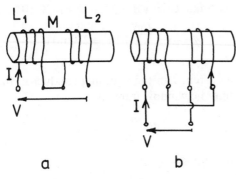

Fig. T16.3

T16.7 ANSWERS AND SOLUTIONS

1. $L_1 = L_2 = M = 96$ mH

2. Assume a current I in the centre conductor. The flux linking the loop formed by the two conductors will be the flux circulating around the space between the conductors, as indicated in the section across the cable which is shown in figure T16.4.

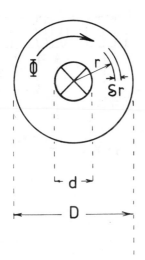

Fig. T16.4

At radius r, where $d/2 < r < D/2$,

$$B_r = \frac{\mu_0 I}{2\pi r}$$

The flux in the thin cylindrical shell of thickness δr is

$$\delta\Phi = B_r l \delta r$$

where l is the length of the cable. The total flux linking the circuit is

$$\Phi = \int_{d/2}^{D/2} \frac{\mu_0 I}{2\pi r} l \, dr = \frac{\mu_0 I}{2\pi r} l \ln(D/d)$$

The inductance per unit length is

$$L = \frac{\Phi}{Il} = \frac{\mu_0}{2\pi} \ln\left(\frac{D}{d}\right)$$

3. Assume a current I in conductor A of figure T16.5 with the direction of positive current into the plane of the paper. The current establishes a flux Φ in the sense shown, and at a general distance x from A we have:

$$B_x = \frac{\mu_0 I}{2\pi x}$$

The flux in the thin shell of thickness δx is

$$\delta\Phi = B_x l \delta x$$

where l is the length of the conductor. The total flux linking the loop AB as a result of the current I in conductor A is:

$$\Phi = \int_r^{d-r} \frac{\mu_0 I}{2\pi x} l \, dx = \frac{\mu_0 I}{2\pi} l \ln\left(\frac{d-r}{r}\right)$$

The current returning along B also establishes a flux which adds to the flux of A between A and B. By symmetry, the magnitudes of these fluxes will be equal so that the total flux linkage of the loop is $\lambda = 2\Phi$.

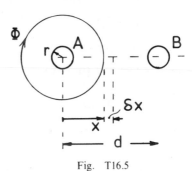

Fig. T16.5

The inductance per metre run is

$$\frac{\lambda}{Il} = \frac{\mu_0}{\pi} \ln\left(\frac{d-r}{r}\right)$$

4. Assume a steady current I in the left-hand conductors of figure T16.6, as shown. Flux linking the loop CD as a result of current I in A is

$$\Phi_A = \int_{r_1}^{r_2} \frac{\mu_0 I l}{2\pi r} \, dr = \frac{\mu_0 I l}{2\pi} \ln\left(\frac{3}{2}\right)$$

(assuming that the conductor radius is small).

Flux linking the loop CD as a result of current I in B is

$$\frac{\mu_0 I l}{2\pi} \ln(2)$$

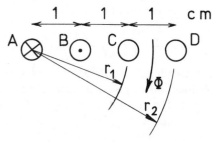

Fig. T16.6

The total flux through CD in an anticlockwise sense about A is:

$$\Phi_T = \Phi_B - \Phi_A = \frac{\mu_0 I l}{2\pi} \ln\left(\frac{4}{3}\right)$$

The mutual inductance per unit length, M_L is Φ_T/Il
The e.m.f. induced per metre run of CD is

$$V = M_L \frac{dI}{dt}$$

$$V = M_L 0.5 \; 2\pi f \cos 2\pi f t$$

and the r.m.s. value is, by substitution, 2.3 mV m^{-1}.

5. From the circuital law,

$$NI = H_i l_i + H_g l_g$$

and by substitution this gives

$$\Phi = 4.88 \; NI \; 10^{-8} \text{ Wb}$$

$$\lambda = 4.88 \; N^2 I \; 10^{-8} \text{ Wb}$$

$$L = \frac{\lambda}{I} = 1.95 \text{ mH}$$

6. $V = 3$ volts

7. The flux through coil B is $1.8 \; 10^{-3} \; 0.6$ Wb

The flux linkage with B is $1500 \; \Phi = 1620 \; 10^{-3}$ Wb

$$M = \frac{\lambda}{I} = \frac{1620}{6} \; 10^{-3} = 270 \text{ mH}$$

8. With a current I in the lightning conductor, the flux threading the window frame is

$$\Phi = \frac{\mu_0 I}{2\pi} \ln 4$$

The mutual inductance,

$$M = \frac{\Phi}{I} = \frac{\mu_0}{2\pi} \ln 4$$

9. (a) See figure T16.7
   (b) For the series aiding case:

$$V = (L_1 + L_2 + 2M) \frac{dI}{dt}$$

for the series opposing case:

$$V = (L_1 + L_2 - 2M) \frac{dI}{dt}$$

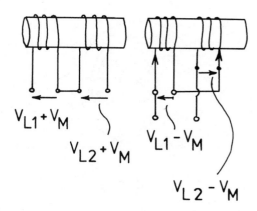

Fig. T16.7

CHAPTER 33

Task 17: Energy storage in the magnetic field

T17.1 INTRODUCTION

In this Task we shall be developing simple models to describe the phenomenon of energy storage in the magnetic field. With these models we can then explain and predict the behaviour of some electromagnetic devices. We shall show that we can think of the energy being stored in the inductance or in the magnetic field about the circuit. We shall also look at the effect of iron and the way in which we allow for the non-linear relationship between B and H. Finally, we shall show how forces in magnetic devices may be determined from a knowledge of the rate of change of stored energy.

T17.2 OBJECTIVES

When you have completed this Task you should be able to:

(a) determine the energy storage associated with a current in an inductive circuit;
(b) determine the energy storage associated with a magnetic field in free space, defined by B and H;
(c) determine the energy storage associated with a magnetic field in iron; and
(d) determine the force developed in an electromagnetic device by considering the change in stored energy within the magnetic field.

T17.3 PRIOR WORK

This Task relies heavily on the work covered in Task 16 and it also makes use of the principle of virtual work which was introduced in Task 7.

T17.4 ENERGY STORED BY CURRENT FLOW IN AN INDUCTIVE CIRCUIT

The equivalent circuit of figure T17.1 represents the case of two magnetically coupled coils when one coil is

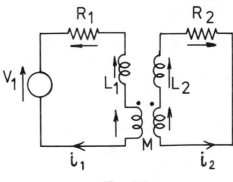

Fig. T17.1

supplied from a time-varying source of voltage v_1. Using the dot convention for current and voltage in coupled circuits, the current i_2 and the voltage $M di_1/dt$ are defined as shown. We can then write:

$$v_1 = i_1 R_1 + L_1 \frac{di_1}{dt} + M \frac{di_2}{dt} \qquad (T17.1)$$

and

$$0 = i_2 R_2 + L_2 \frac{di_2}{dt} + M \frac{di_1}{dt} \qquad (T17.2)$$

If we multiply Equation T17.1 by i_1, Equation T17.2 by i_2, add and rearrange we obtain:

$$v_1 i_1 = i_1^2 R_1 + i_2^2 R_2 + \frac{d}{dt}\left(\frac{1}{2} L_1 i_1^2\right) + \frac{d}{dt}\left(\frac{1}{2} L_2 i_2^2\right)$$
$$+ \frac{d}{dt}(M i_1 i_2)$$

We can readily identify the rate of energy input to the circuit, $v_1 i_1$, and the rate of energy loss, $i_1^2 R_1 + i_2^2 R_2$.

The remaining terms represent the rate of energy storage. We can therefore identify three stores of energy:

(1) $\frac{1}{2} L_1 i_1^2$ in the inductance L_1

(2) $\frac{1}{2} L_2 i_2^2$ in the inductance L_2 and

(3) $M i_1 i_2$ in the mutual inductance M.

We can use our previous definition of inductance, $L =$ flux linkages per ampere, to rewrite the equations for energy storage as:

$$\frac{1}{2} L_1 i_1^2 = \frac{1}{2} \lambda_1 i_1 = \frac{1}{2} \Phi_1 i_1 \quad \text{if} \quad N_1 = 1$$

$$\frac{1}{2} L_2 i_2^2 = \frac{1}{2} \lambda_2 i_2 = \frac{1}{2} \Phi_2 i_2 \quad \text{if} \quad N_2 = 1$$

and

$$M_1 i_1 i_2 = \lambda_m i_2 = \Phi_m i_2$$

T17.5 ENERGY STORED IN A LINEAR MAGNETIC CIRCUIT

Starting with the core of figure T17.2 unmagnetised, we can store up energy by building up a current and creating a magnetic field.

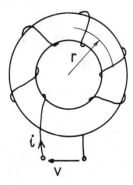

Fig. T17.2

The field energy comes from the electric circuit and the electrical input energy is:

$$W = \int_0^t Vi \, dt = \int_0^t N \frac{d\Phi}{dt} i \, dt = \int_0^\Phi Ni \, d\Phi$$

but $Ni = Hl$ and $d\Phi = A \, dB$, where l and A are the mean length and cross-sectional area of the iron core. Therefore,

$$W = \int_0^B lAH \, dB = lA \int_0^B H \, dB \quad (T17.3)$$

If the relationship between H and B is a linear one, then we can write $B = \mu H$ and

$$W = \frac{lA}{\mu} \int_0^B B \, dB = \frac{lAB^2}{2\mu}$$

For the circuit of figure T17.2, since

$$Ni = Hl$$

and

$$\Phi = BA$$

$$W = \frac{1}{2} Ni\Phi = \frac{1}{2} i\lambda = \frac{1}{2} Li^2$$

We see then that in a medium in which there is a linear relationship between B and H we can describe the energy stored either in terms of circuit parameters, $1/2 Li^2$, or in terms of field parameters $1/2 BHlA$.

T17.6 ENERGY STORED IN A NON-LINEAR MAGNETIC CIRCUIT

When the relationship between B and H is non-linear we are left with equation T17.3 from which we define the energy storage per unit volume as

$$U = \int_0^{B_1} H \, dB \quad (T17.4)$$

The graphical interpretation of this is shown in figure T17.3a where the shaded area is equal to U.

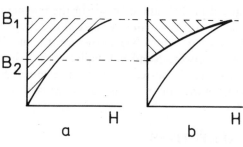

Fig. T17.3

In the normal case of a non-linear magnetic material there is hysteresis and as H decreases from the value shown in figure T17.3a to zero the characteristic follows the curve shown in figure T17.3b. The energy stored per unit during this change is

$$U_1 = \int_{B_1}^{B_2} H \, dB$$

For the purpose of our argument let us assume that the characteristic over this region approximates to the straight line, $B = \mu H + B_2$.

$$U = \int_{B_1}^{B_2} \frac{(B - B_2)}{\mu} dB = -\frac{1}{2\mu} (B_2 - B_1)^2$$

The sign tells us that stored energy is being taken from the magnetic field and the magnitude of the change in U is equal to the area shaded in figure T17.3b. It is easy to see that the energy that has gone into establishing the field is greater than the energy released by the field and in this case the difference cannot be recovered. It represents the energy lost in magnetising the iron core. If we traverse the whole of a hysteresis cycle the energy lost per unit volume of material is equal to the area enclosed by the B-H loop. This is the hysteresis loss.

T17.7 DETERMINATION OF FORCE FROM ENERGY CONSIDERATIONS

We shall take the magnetic circuit of figure T17.4 as our example and assume that the iron has a very large relative permeability so that the inductance of the coil is given approximately by

$$L = N^2 \frac{\mu A}{x}$$

Let us now apply the principle of virtual work and attempt to move the sliding pole piece P through an incremental distance δx by applying a force F in the sense shown. The mechanical work done is then $F\delta x$.

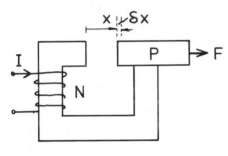

Fig. T17.4

Let us now try an energy balance. There are two energy stores in addition to the mechanical system. One is the field system with an energy store of $\frac{1}{2}\Phi I = \frac{1}{2}LI^2$ and the other is the current source which we shall assume gives us a constant current I.

(i) *Change in stored energy*

As x increases by an amount δx the inductance will decrease by an amount δL. The stored energy decreases by an amount

$$\delta W_F = \frac{1}{2} I^2 \delta L$$

(ii) *Change in source energy*

As x increases by δx, the reluctance $x/\mu A$ increases and for constant NI the flux in the circuit will tend to fall by $\delta\Phi$. This causes a change in flux linkage and this produces a voltage $\delta\lambda/\delta t$ in the coil. The sense of the voltage is such that it will tend to cause a current flow which will oppose the change in flux $\delta\Phi$. Thus the voltage induced will support the current I and, in terms of circuit theory, the coil is acting as a source. The magnetic system is thus attempting to return energy to the supply. The amount provided is

$$VI\delta t = I \frac{\delta L}{\delta t} I\delta t = I^2 \delta L$$

We now have $I^2\delta L$ going into the supply system and only $\frac{1}{2}I^2\delta L$ coming out of the field store. The additional $\frac{1}{2}I^2\delta L$ must be coming from the mechanical system. Thus

$$F\delta x = \frac{1}{2} I^2 \delta L$$

or

$$F = \frac{1}{2} I^2 \frac{\delta L}{\delta x}$$

in the limit as δx tends to zero.

$$F = \frac{1}{2} I^2 \frac{dL}{dx} = \frac{dW_F}{dx}$$

This tells us that we need to apply a force F and do work when moving the bar in the direction of positive x. In other words the system is trying to move the bar in the direction of negative x. If we allow this to happen, then the inductance will increase, the reluctance will decrease and, for constant current, the flux will increase. The system appears then to be trying to increase the flux linkages. This is a result which has general application; any magnetic circuit will tend to adjust its position, or shape, so that the product $I\Phi$ has a maximum value—where Φ is measured positively when it has a right-hand rotation about I.

T17.8 THE FORCE OF ATTRACTION BETWEEN MAGNETISED IRON SURFACES

Take a magnetic circuit such as shown in figure T17.5 and move the straight bar a distance δx by the action of the force F. Assume that δx is so small that the flux density in the circuit is unchanged. The energy stored in the iron circuit is then unchanged, but the energy stored in the airgap is increased by an amount

$$\delta W = \frac{1}{2} BHA\delta x$$

where $A/2$ is the pole area.

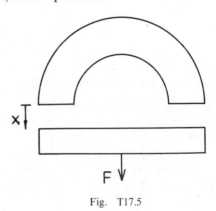

Fig. T17.5

This change in stored energy is equal in magnitude to the work done, so that

$$F\delta x = \frac{1}{2} BHA\delta x$$

and

$$F = \frac{1}{2} BHA$$

T17.9   SELF-ASSESSMENT QUESTIONS

Question 1

A long flat stator has a series of current-carrying coils embedded in it such that the magnetic flux density in the space about the stator varies along the stator in the manner shown in figure T17.6. The flux is not time varying.

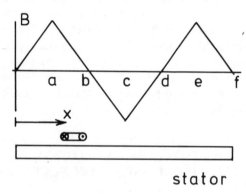

Fig.   T17.6

A rectangular conducting loop is placed on top of the stator and is free to move in either direction along the x axis. A direct current flows in the loop in such a sense that the flux produced by the coil acts down into the stator.

Determine the positions at which the coil will be in stable equilibrium.

Question 2

Figure T17.7 represents a trolley which carries a conducting coil AB and is free to run on a non-magnetic surface between the poles of a large permanent magnet.

(a) Given the direction of current in the coil decide whether or not the trolley will move. Base your argument on energy considerations.
(b) The second coil, CD, is now excited so that a steady current flows into D and out of C. Predict what will happen to the trolley, assuming a loss-less system.

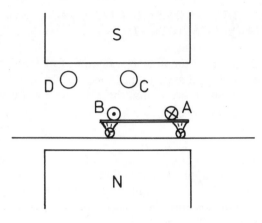

Fig.   T17.7

Question 3

An electromagnetic relay is wound with 600 turns and is supplied from a constant-current source of 0.1A. The effective cross-sectional area of the air gap is 4 cm². The inductance of the relay is given approximately by $L = \mu_0 N^2 A / x$, where N is the number of turns on the exciting winding, A is the effective cross-sectional area of the airgap and x is the gap length.

(a) Plot a scaled graph of force on the relay armature against gap length x from $x=0$ to $x=1$ cm. Explain any extreme features of the graph.
(b) Given that the relay winding resistance is 800 Ω and assuming that the relay is restricted to close at a constant velocity of 1 m s⁻¹ plot a scaled graph of voltage across the exciting winding against gap length x from $x=0$ to $x=1$ cm.

Question 4

An electromagnet has an airgap of cross-sectional area 500 cm² and 4 mm long. Determine the energy stored in the magnetic field in the airgap when a current of 10 A exists in the 300 turns of the magnet coil.

Question 5

The electromagnet for a contactor has an airgap of cross-sectional area 20 cm² and length 5 mm. The m.m.f. across the airgap is 3000 A. Determine the force tending to close the airgap.

Question 6

Figure T17.8 shows a section through a cylindrical magnet. The coil has an inductance of 0.5 H when the

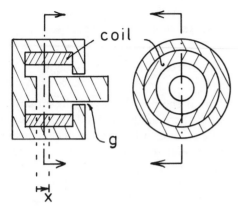

Fig.   T17.8

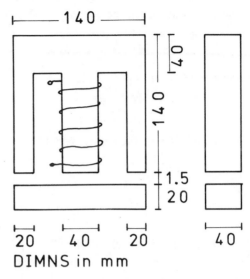

DIMNS in mm

Fig.   T17.9

airgap x is 7 mm and a constant current of 1 A flows in the coil. The cross-sectional area of the plunger is 12 cm^2 and the gap g is negligible compared with x. Determine

(a) the force on the armature when $x=7$ mm;
(b) the force on the armature when $x=3$ mm; and
(c) the mechanical work done as the armature moves from $x=7$ mm to $x=3$ mm.

Question 7

The supply to the magnet shown in figure T17.8 is controlled so that the flux density in the airgap remains constant at 0.3 T. Determine

(a) the force on the armature when $x=6$ mm;
(b) the force on the armature when $x=3$ mm;
(c) the mechanical work done as the armature moves from $x=6$ mm to $x=3$ mm; and
(d) the change in energy stored in the magnetic field.

Question 8

The force required on the yoke of the electromagnet shown in figure T17.9 is 800 N. Determine the necessary ampere-turns for the coil on the control limb. Magnetic leakage and fringing at the airgaps may be neglected.

The following figures are taken from the magnetisation curve for the steel used in the magnet construction

H(Am^{-1})	100	210	340	500	600	800
B(T)	0.2	0.4	0.6	0.8	0.9	1.0

T17.10   SOLUTIONS

1. The coil will tend to move to a position of maximum flux linkage. This occurs in position C.

2. (a) The coil AB produces a flux which is vertically upwards and in the same sense as the flux of the

permanent magnet. Assuming a uniform field distribution, the coil is already in a position of maximum flux linkage and will not tend to move.

(b) Coil CD will tend to weaken the flux through coil AB in the region near B. The coil will therefore tend to move to the right since it 'sees' a larger positive field about A than about B. Assuming no friction, the coil will overshoot and side A will leave the region of the permanent field. Moving in this sense, the coil experiences a reducing flux linkage and the forces on the coil tend to decelerate it and reverse its motion so that it moves back into the field. Whether or not it does reverse depends on the relative magnitudes of the fields of the coil CD and the permanent magnet.

3. (a) Force $F = \dfrac{\mathrm{d}}{\mathrm{d}x} W_F = \dfrac{\mathrm{d}}{\mathrm{d}x}\left(\dfrac{1}{2}\dfrac{\mu_0 N^2 A}{x} I^2\right)$

$$= -\frac{905\ 10^{-9}}{x^2}\ \mathrm{N}$$

(remember, F was defined in the sense of increasing x)

$-F$	∞	226	56	25	14	9	10^{-3} N
x	0	2	4	6	8	10	mm

Clearly we cannot accept that $F \to \infty$ as $x \to 0$, otherwise we could never open a relay contact so long as any residual magnetism existed. The solution tends to infinity because of the approximation for L, which ignores the reluctance of the iron path.

(b) The e.m.f. induced in the coil is given by $d\lambda/dt$

$$\frac{d\lambda}{dt} = \frac{d}{dt}(LI) = L\frac{dI}{dt} + I\frac{dL}{dt}$$

and since I is constant

$$\frac{d\lambda}{dt} = I\frac{dL}{dt} = I\frac{dL}{dx}\frac{dx}{dt}$$

The voltage across the coil is given by:

$$V = IR + \frac{d\lambda}{dt}$$

$$V = 80 + \frac{18}{x^2}10^{-6} \text{ volts}$$

V	∞	84.52	81.13	80.50	80.28	80.18	volts
x	0	2	4	6	8	10	mm

4. $NI = 3000$ A; $H_g = \dfrac{NI}{l_g}$; $B_g = \mu_0 H_g$;

$W_F = \frac{1}{2}B_g H_g l_g A_g = 70.7$ J

The reluctance of the iron is neglected.

5. $F = \frac{1}{2}BHA = 450$ N

6. (a) Ignoring the reluctance of the core, the inductance is inversely proportional to x,

$$L = \frac{k}{x} \quad \text{and} \quad k = 0.5\,7\,10^{-3}$$

$$\therefore F = \frac{d}{dx}\left(\frac{1}{2}LI^2\right) = -35.7 \text{ N}$$

(b) $F = -194.4$ N

(c) The work done by the magnet equals the change in stored energy:

$$WD = \frac{1}{2}L_1 I^2 - \frac{1}{2}L_2 I^2 = 192 \text{ mJ}$$

7. (a) & (b) If the flux density in the airgap does not change there can be no e.m.f. induced in the coil, so that no energy transfer occurs between the magnet and the supply. In this case the energy to do work comes out of the field energy and $F = d/dx\,W_F$.

In terms of field quantities

$$W_F = \frac{1}{2}BHAx$$

$$\frac{dW_F}{dx} = \frac{1}{2}BHA = 43 \text{ N}$$

(c) $WD = $ change in stored energy
$WD = \frac{1}{2}BHA(x_1 - x_2) = 0.13$ J

(d) Change in stored energy $= -0.13$ J

8. $F = 800 = \dfrac{1}{2}\dfrac{B^2 A}{\mu_0}$ N

$\therefore B = 0.79$ T

Using the circuital law around one half of the circuit,

$$NI = H_i\,380\,10^{-3} + H_g\,3\,10^{-3}$$

and

$$H_i = 500 \text{ Am}^{-1}, \quad B_g = \mu_0 H_g,$$

$$\therefore NI = 1890 + 190 = 2080 \text{ A}$$

CHAPTER 34

a.c. machinery

34.1 INTRODUCTION

Not very many years ago it was fashionable to explain all electrical machine operations in terms of a generalised theory of electrical machines. This approach has since fallen into disfavour, except in specialist courses, because it tended to cloud rather than clarify the subject for the beginner. The philosophy was sound enough because the behaviour of all electromagnetic machines does depend on a common set of fundamental principles which are not too difficult to understand. It may indeed surprise you to know that you have covered these principles in the various Tasks that you have already completed.

Energy storage, for example, leads us to the equation for energy balance in electromagnetic devices:

Change in electrical energy input = Mechanical work done + Change in stored energy in field

As a power equation this becomes,

$$P_e = P_m + \frac{\mathrm{d}}{\mathrm{d}t} W_f$$

and it holds for all electromagnetic machines.

We know that W_F can be written in terms of field quantities or circuit parameters so that we can at least appreciate how a detailed machine analysis might proceed even if we cannot yet do it. Then we have Faraday's law, which is crucial to understanding how e.m.f.s are produced in machines and finally there is the principle which we deduced in the last Task that electromagnetic systems tend to move to maximise the flux linkage in the circuit.

Let us see if we can put some of these ideas together to explain the operation of some common, and some not so common electric motors.

34.2 THE INDUCTION MACHINE

Let us start where most people finish, with a linear machine. Figure 34.1a shows a stator with a single turn coil above it which is restricted to move parallel to the stator. Figure 34.1b shows the distribution of

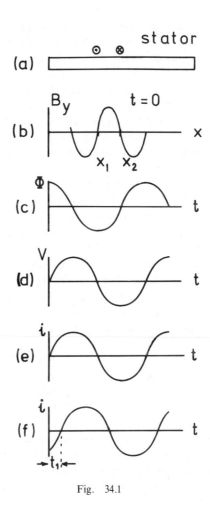

Fig. 34.1

flux density above the stator at an instant in time $t = 0$: note that the coil spans a half wave of the flux density pattern. Let us imagine that the flux density pattern is travelling from right to left in the sense of decreasing x; this will cause a change in flux linking the coil and a plot of flux linkage with time would appear as in figure 34.1c.

The voltage induced in the coil is $\mathrm{d}\Phi/\mathrm{d}t$ and is assumed positive when acting around the coil in the sense indicated in figure 34.1a. The variation of V with time is shown in figure 34.1d.

The voltage V causes a current flow i in the coil in the same sense as V and in time phase with V if we assume that the coil is a pure resistance.

Summarising conditions at $t = 0$, we have maximum flux through the coil in an upward sense, zero voltage in the coil and zero current.

At a time $t = \Delta t$ the flux density pattern will have moved a distance Δx to the left, the flux through the coil will be falling and v and i will be increasing positive. At this instant, then, the current induced in the coil is producing a small flux acting upwards and, if free to move, the coil will try maximise its linkage with other flux in the upwards sense. The peak of positive flux is however moving off to the left and the coil will therefore try to move with it. This is inductor motor action and it is a simple enough exercise to translate figure 34.1 into a cylindrical geometry.

If the coil has inductance, which it certainly will have in a real case, the current in the coil will lag the voltage by some angle α corresponding to a time lag t_1 as in figure 34.1f. At time $t = \Delta t$ the current is negative and the coil tries to link with flux in the downward sense, i.e. it will try to move to the right to align with the maximum negative flux of the exciting system. Only when the current goes positive does the force on the coil tend to drive it in the same sense as the moving field. The larger the angle α, the smaller is the nett force on the coil in the sense of decreasing x. The ratio of R/X for the coil should be high if we want a large torque and we can see from this why many induction motors have resistance added to the rotor circuit to increase the torque on starting.

At operating speeds, the coil in figure 34.1 will be moving at nearly the same speed as the flux density pattern and the frequency of the induced e.m.f. in the coil will be very low. The reactance effect will also be small, since $X = 2\pi f L$, and angle α will be small. In this case we can afford to have a small coil resistance so that the current in the coil and the torque on the coil will be large. It would appear that the extra resistance put in for starting should be switched out for satisfactory operation at high speeds.

34.3 SHADED POLE ACTION

The travelling field of figure 34.1b is best obtained with a stator winding which is fed from a three-phase a.c. supply, but in many applications only a single-phase a.c. supply is available. Can we then make an induction motor to operate under these conditions? A simplified representation of a field system for a single-phase machine is shown in figure 34.2 and if the exciting current i is sinusoidally varying with time then the field between the pole pieces simply changes magnitude with

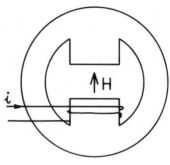

Fig. 34.2

time—it does not change direction. It would seem then that there is no moving field pattern in the machine and therefore the arguments of the previous section cannot apply. But, it is possible to represent the pulsating magnetic field strength H in figure 34.2 by two rotating components, each of magnitude $H/2$, one rotating clockwise and the other anticlockwise. Figure 34.3 illustrates the idea.

We can now apply the argument of the previous section to each moving field pattern and we find that a coil such as the one shown in figure 34.1a does indeed try to follow the field pattern moving to the left—let us assume that this represents 'anticlockwise'—but, unfortunately, it also tries to follow the pattern moving to the right. This brings us back to where we were, with a machine that doesn't work.

However, let us suppose that the coil does move off to the left in figure 34.1 at a speed not much less than the speed of the field pattern which is moving that way. All the conditions described in figure 34.1 hold true and the current in the coil due to the anticlockwise field is almost in phase with the voltage because the reactance of the coil is very small. The speed of the coil with respect to the clockwise field pattern is about twice the speed of the coil with respect to the stator and the frequently of the e.m.f. induced in the coil by the clockwise field is relatively high. The current produced in the coil by this e.m.f. is small because $X = 2\pi f L$ is high and the nett clockwise torque is further reduced because the angle α, or time lag t_1, is high. The machine therefore develops a nett anticlockwise torque at speed, if only we can get it going.

Figure 34.4 shows the single coil directly beneath the poles of the stator. The flux Φ through the coil and the current induced in the coil are also shown as functions of time when the coil is purely resistive. The figure also shows a copper sheet S which has been placed in the airgap between the pole piece and the coil. There will be a current induced around this sheet in the same way as current is induced in the coil. It will be in time-phase with the coil current and will try to delay the fall in the flux as time increases from $t = 0$. The flux in the region

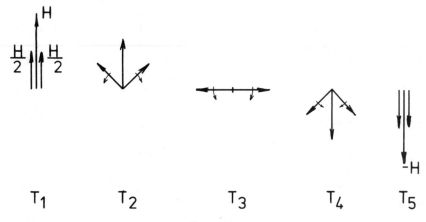

Fig. 34.3

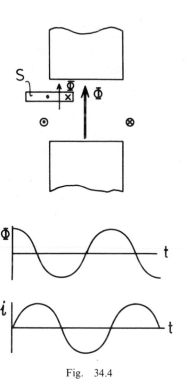

Fig. 34.4

the sheet grows, the sheet will attempt to maximise flux linkage in the positive sense with respect to this current. In the position it occupies in figure 34.4 it will find the flux linkage dropping rapidly as the main flux falls to zero. The sheet therefore tends to move out of this falling field. If it is not rigidly fixed it will eject itself out of the airgap in the same direction as the single coil. With the sheet in position the pole is said to be shaded.

In practical shaded pole machines the copper sheet is replaced by a copper loop which is wrapped around a part of the pole piece as shown in figure 34.5.

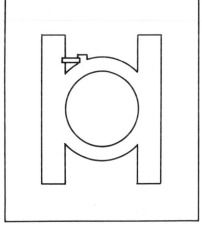

Fig. 34.5

above and below the sheet will therefore fall off less rapidly than the flux on the main axis of the pole. The effect of this is that the line of maximum flux density shifts from the main axis of the pole piece towards the position of the copper sheet. The single coil sees this shift as an anticlockwise movement of the field pattern and it begins to follow it. Once the coil is moving it will develop more torque in the anticlockwise sense than in the clockwise sense and the coil will accelerate to approach the speed of the field pattern.

In energy terms, the single coil sees a greater positive flux linkage to the left of centre than at the centre and it moves to maximise its flux linkage. By a similar argument we can predict what would happen to the copper sheet if it were not rigidly fixed. As the current around

34.4 RACK AND PINION MOTORS

Suppose that we have a conducting coil which is free to rotate about an axis as shown in figure 34.6. Let us establish a magnetic field strength H which acts perpendicularly to the plane of the coil at an instant $t=0$ and which rotates in a clockwise sense with a steady angular velocity. The flux through the coil then varies

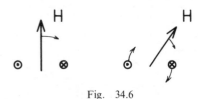

Fig. 34.6

with time in the manner of figure 34.1c and the current varies as figure 34.1e, if the loop is resistive. As the axis of H varies from position 1 to position 2 in figure 34.6, the flux through the loop falls and the current in the loop increases. The loop tries to establish maximum flux linkage in a positive sense about i and to do so it tends to rotate in a clockwise fashion to keep the axis of H perpendicular to the plane of the coil. A copper cylinder placed with its long axes along the axis of rotation of the coil in figure 34.6 will also rotate in a clockwise sense

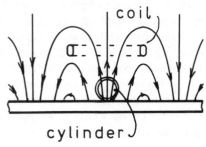

Fig. 34.7

because of currents induced in the closed conducting paths around the cylinder walls.

Let us now take the field pattern shown in figure 34.7 and assume that it is travelling from right to left. We will place two objects in the field: one a single-turn coil; the other a copper cylinder which is free to rotate about its long axis. Both are restricted to move parallel to the stator plane.

In which direction does each object try to move?

The coil should present no difficulty because the situation is very similar to that of figure 34.1 and we would expect the coil to follow the field to the left.

The behaviour of the cylinder is not so obvious. The first point to establish is the nature of the field change in the region around the cylinder. If the cylinder remains stationary, then as the field moves past it to the left we would see the field across the cylinder changing in the manner shown in figure 34.8. As far as the cylinder is concerned this is a clockwise rotating field and following our previous argument we would expect to see the cylinder rotate in a clockwise sense and roll along the stator to the right. This it will do.

The most striking examples of this kind of action are demonstrated by Professor E. R. Laithwaite in a film with the title *Motor Big and Small*. This is available from the ICI film library and can be recommended for showing to any engineering or science society.

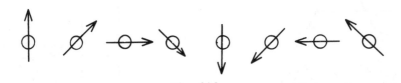

Fig. 34.8

CHAPTER 35

Task 18: The transformer

T18.1 INTRODUCTION

A transformer consists essentially of two or more coils which share a common magnetic circuit, i.e. they are electromagnetically coupled. One coil, usually called the primary, is connected to a time-varying voltage source while the other coils are connected to load circuits.

The magnetic circuit of a power transformer which will operate at power frequencies of 50 or 60 Hz, is built up of laminated steel sheets. This is to keep the losses in the transformer down to reasonable levels. However, the losses increase substantially with frequency and for high frequency work the core may well have to be made from a ferrite or even a nonferromagnetic material. In practice transformers vary in size from the very small, for use in deaf-aids, to the largest power transformer which will have a rating in excess of 1000 MV A. The largest will dwarf a double-decker bus.

In this Task we shall examine the principles which govern the operation of the transformer and we shall assume that all voltage waveforms are sinusoidal. We shall also neglect the effects of resistance in the windings and the effect of magnetic flux leakage.

T18.2 OBJECTIVES

When you have finished this Task you should be able to:
(a) explain to the satisfaction of a fellow student how a transformer works;
(b) calculate the primary current from a knowledge of secondary current and turns ratio;
(c) calculate secondary voltage from a knowledge of primary voltage and turns ratio;
(d) determine the number of turns required on the primary and secondary windings given the frequency, the required voltages and the flux level in the core;
(e) refer secondary impedances to the primary circuit, and vice-versa; and
(f) determine the core area when the maximum operating flux density, the primary voltage and frequency, and the primary turns are given.

T18.3 PRIOR WORK

The work covered in this Task follows on from Tasks 15 and 16 and it is assumed that you are familiar with simple a.c. circuit theory.

T18.4 SYMBOLS AND CONVENTIONS

In order to avoid confusion over signs and phase shifts we shall define our terminology very carefully. In general, we shall use lower case letters to represent instantaneous values and capitals to represent r.m.s. and maximum values.

v_1 instantaneous voltage applied to primary winding
e_1 instantaneous self-induced e.m.f. in primary winding
v_2 instantaneous voltage across secondary terminals
e_2 instantaneous e.m.f. induced in secondary winding
i_0 instantaneous magnetising current in primary
Φ instantaneous mutual flux linking primary and secondary
V_1 r.m.s. voltage applied to primary
V_{1M} maximum voltage applied to primary
V_2 r.m.s. voltage across secondary terminals
V_{2M} maximum voltage across secondary terminals
E r.m.s. value of e.m.f.

The conventions that we shall adopt for the assumed directions of positive voltage, current, flux and e.m.f. are clearly shown in figure T18.1.

T18.5 THE TRANSFORMER EFFECT

If we apply a time-varying voltage v_1 to the primary winding of the circuit shown in figure T18.1 a current i_0 will flow in the N_1 turns of the winding to establish a flux Φ in the magnetic circuit. The flux Φ is known as the

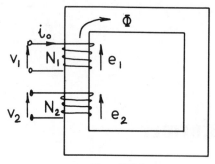

Fig. T18.1

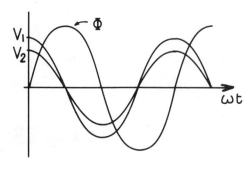

Fig. T18.2

mutual flux because it links both the primary and secondary coils. There will be an induced e.m.f. e_1 in the primary winding and an induced e.m.f. e_2 in the secondary winding and both will be proportional to the rate of change of flux.

If v_1 is rising positive, e_1 and e_2 will also be rising positive in the sense indicated in figure T18.1. Neglecting resistance

$$v_1 = e_1 = N_1 \frac{d\Phi}{dt}$$

and

$$e_2 = N_2 \frac{d\Phi}{dt}$$

The e.m.f. e_2 appears across the secondary terminals as the terminal voltage v_2 and it follows that

$$\frac{v_1}{v_2} = \frac{N_1}{N_2}$$

Expressed differently, this tells us that the voltage per turn is the same for each winding, i.e.

$$\frac{v_1}{N_1} = \frac{v_2}{N_2} = \frac{d\Phi}{dt}$$

T18.6 THE TRANSFORMER e.m.f. EQUATION

If we assume that the flux in the core is sinusoidal and can be represented by $\Phi = \Phi_m \sin \omega t$ then

$$v_1 = e_1 = N_1 \frac{d\Phi}{dt} = N_1 \omega \Phi_m \cos \omega t$$

and

$$v_2 = e_2 = N_2 \omega \Phi_m \cos \omega t$$

We see that v_1 and v_2 are in phase and lead the flux phasor Φ by $\pi/2$ radians as shown in figure T18.2. From the two previous equations we can write,

$$V_1 = \frac{1}{\sqrt{2}} N_1 2\pi f \Phi_m = 4.44 f \Phi_m N_1$$

and

$$V_2 = 4.44 f \Phi_m N_2$$

Note in particular that $V_1 \propto f \Phi_m N_1$. For a given number of turns N_1, the flux Φ_m is determined by the applied voltage V_1 and the frequency f.

T18.7 THE TRANSFORMER ON LOAD

If a circuit is connected across the terminals of the secondary winding then a current i_2 will flow in the secondary circuit. The magnitude of this current and its phase relationship to v_2 will be determined by the nature of the load circuit. Referring to figure T18.3 we can see that i_2 will flow in a sense which will produce an m.m.f. $i_2 N_2$ which opposes the m.m.f. of the magnetising current, $i_0 N_1$. The tendency is to reduce the mutual flux Φ, but we have seen that Φ is fixed by V_1 and f, so what happens?

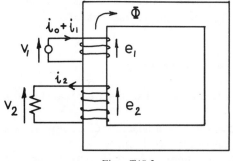

Fig. T18.3

Momentarily, as i_2 commences, the flux Φ reduces slightly. This causes a reduction in e_1 and $v_1 - e_1$ is no longer zero. An additional current i_1 now flows in the primary winding such that $i_1 N_1 = i_2 N_2$ and since the two m.m.f.s are in opposition their resultant is zero and Φ returns to its original value. In effect, a current i_2 in the secondary winding demands a current i_1 in the primary winding such that $i_1 N_1 = i_2 N_2$.

The total primary current can be considered as having

two components: the original magnetising current i_0 and the load component i_1. These components will normally be out of phase with each other and their sum is a phasor sum. When the transformer is carrying its full load current, i_0 will be very small in comparison with i_1 and it is often sufficient to regard i_1 as the total primary current. On this assumption,

$$i_1 N_1 = i_2 N_2$$

and

$$\frac{i_1}{i_2} = \frac{N_2}{N_1} = \frac{v}{v_1}$$

hence

$$v_1 i_1 = v_2 i_2$$

and the volt-ampere input equals the volt-ampere output.

T18.8 THE TRANSFORMER AS A CIRCUIT ELEMENT

Given a secondary load impedance Z_2 the r.m.s. secondary current is $I_2 = V_2/Z_2$.

The source supplying the transformer provides a current I_1 at a potential V_1 and effectively sees an impedance at the primary terminals of $V_1/I_1 = Z_1$. This can be written in terms of secondary equations as:

$$Z_1 = \frac{V_1}{I_1} = \frac{N_1 V_2}{N_2} \frac{N_1}{N_2 I_2} = \frac{V_2}{I_2} \frac{N_1^2}{N_2^2} = Z_2 \frac{N_1^2}{N_2^2}$$

This effect is used for impedance matching.

T18.9 THE TRANSFORMER AS A MUTUALLY COUPLED CIRCUIT

The transformer may be represented by the equivalent circuit of figure T18.4 and using the parameters defined there

$$V_1 = L_1 \frac{\mathrm{d}}{\mathrm{d}t}(i_1 + i_0) - M \frac{\mathrm{d}}{\mathrm{d}t} i_2$$

$$= L_1 \frac{\mathrm{d}i_0}{\mathrm{d}t} + \left(L_1 \frac{\mathrm{d}i_1}{\mathrm{d}t} - M \frac{\mathrm{d}i_2}{\mathrm{d}t} \right)$$

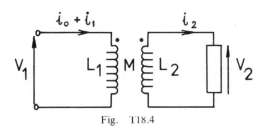

Fig. T18.4

Using the definitions of inductance, $L_1 = \lambda_1/i_1$ and $M = \lambda_2/i_1$, and the known ratio of the primary and secondary currents, you should be able to prove that the expression in brackets is zero. Thus, $V_1 = L_1 \, \mathrm{d}i_0/\mathrm{d}t = e_1$ as before.

Because the e.m.f. e_1 is produced by the current i_0 in the self inductance L_1 it is possible to separate the currents i_0 and i_1 and consider them as flowing in separate paths, as in figure T18.5. This is an artificial separation but it does lead towards a model circuit for a real transformer.

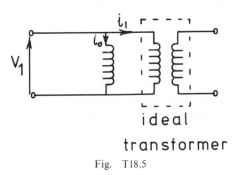

ideal transformer

Fig. T18.5

T18.10 SELF-ASSESSMENT EQUATIONS

Question 1

A transformer is used to connect two a.c. systems which operate at 23.34 kV and 7.78 kV. Determine the turns ratio.

Question 2

A transformer supplies an alternating current of 500 mA at 6.25 V. The primary supply voltage is 240, determine the primary current.

Question 3

A transformer supplies three, 1 kW electric fires in parallel at a voltage of 240 V. Determine the input VA to the transformer.

Question 4

The output impedance of one circuit is 8 Ω. The input impedance of another is 5 Ω. Determine the turns ratio of the transformer required between the two circuits for matching.

Question 5

A transformer has 100 turns on the primary and 5 turns on the secondary. Determine the primary equivalent of the following secondary loads:

(a) a resistance of 1 kΩ
(b) an inductance of 5 mH
(c) a capacitance of 1 μF
(d) an impedance of $(5+j7)$ Ω

Question 6

A transformer is to operate from a 200 V, 50 Hz supply and the maximum flux density in the core must not exceed 1.4 T. Determine the minimum core cross-section for a 100 turn primary coil.

Question 7

A transformer is designed for a primary voltage of 240 V at a frequency of 60 Hz. The maximum flux density in the core is then 1.4 T. Determine

(a) the maximum flux density in the core when the supply is 240 V at 50 Hz, and
(b) the supply voltage which will produce a maximum flux density of 1.4 T at 50 Hz.

Question 8

Determine the number of turns required for the primary and secondary windings of a 6600/250 V, 50 Hz transformer if the maximum flux density in the core is not to exceed 1.5 T. The effective cross-sectional area of the core is 0.023 m².

If the 250 V terminals are connected to a load of 50 kVA with a lagging phase angle of 60° determine the current in the 6600 V winding. Assume that the magnetising current is 0.5 A.

T18.11 ANSWERS AND SOLUTIONS

1. 3:1

2. $I_1 = 13$ mA

3. $VA_1 = 3$ kVA

4. $N_1 = 1.265 N_2$

5. (a) $Z_{1e} = Z_2 \dfrac{N_1^2}{N_2^2} = Z_2\, 400$

$\therefore R_{1e} = 400$ kΩ

(b) $\omega L_{1e} = \omega L_2 \times 400, \therefore L_{1e} = 2$ H

(c) $\dfrac{1}{\omega C_{1e}} = \dfrac{1}{\omega C_2} 400 \therefore C_{1e} = 2500$ pF

(d) $Z_{1e} = (5+j7)\,400 = (2+j2.8)$ kΩ

6. $V_1 = 4.44\, BAfN_1$

$\therefore A = 64.3$ cm²

7. $V_1 = 4.44\, BAf N_1$

(a) $B_A f_A = B_B f_B \quad \therefore B_B = 1.68$ T

(b) $\dfrac{V_A}{f_A} = \dfrac{V_B}{f_B} \qquad \therefore V_B = 200$ V

8. $V_1 = 6600 = 4.44\, BAN_1 f$

$\therefore N_1 = 861.7$, but we cannot have partial turns so that
$N_1 = 861$ or 862.

If $N_1 = 861$, $B_{max} = 1.501$

if $N_1 = 862$, $B_{max} = 1.499$

The choice is therefore open and we can select $N_1 = 861$ if we wish since the error in B_{max} is negligible. $V_2 = 250 = 4.44\, B_m AN_2 f$

$N_2 = 32.6$ and we must choose $N_2 = 32$ or 33.

Let $N_2 = 32$, then $V_2 = 254.3$ V

let $N_2 = 33$, then $V_2 = 252.96$ V

The second solution is closer to the required value for V_2 and provided $V_2 = 250$ is not an absolute upper limit we can select $N_2 = 33$.

$V_2 \simeq 253$ V, and the secondary load is 50 (cos 60 +j sin 60) 10^3 VA which gives a current $I_2 = 50/253$ $(0.5 - j0.866)\, 10^3$ A.

(remember Power $= VI$).

$\therefore I_1 = \dfrac{N_2 I_2}{I_1} = 3.787 - j6.560$ A

the total primary current $= \bar{I}_1 + \bar{I}_0 = (3.8 - j7.1)$ A

A preferred solution would be to state $VA_1 = VA_2$

$\therefore I_1 = \dfrac{VA}{V_1} = 3.787 - j6.560$ etc.

CHAPTER 36

More about the transformer

36.1 INTRODUCTION

At first sight the transformer appears to be such a straightforward piece of equipment that it hardly deserves further study. Take efficiency as an example. A large transformer may well run at 99% efficiency, given the right circumstances, and it is difficult to see this figure being increased. But 1% of, say, 1000 MW is an awful lot of power to be dissipated and the impact of this one problem alone on the design of a large transformer is considerable. Then there is the winding to consider. When the normal load current is measured in thousands of amperes the forces between adjacent conductors cannot be ignored and if transient currents well in excess of normal load values have to be allowed for then the mechanical bracing system needs careful design. This in turn relies on careful analysis by the electrical engineer who will be expected to provide a detailed specification of the complex pattern of forces acting on the transformer structure. As if this were not enough, we then discover that the transmission engineer, interested in co-ordinating the lightning protection scheme around a high-voltage substation, insists that the transformer acts as a capacitance divider under transient conditions. We can see then that the theory of the previous chapter is only an introduction to a complex subject.

36.2 SOME PROBLEMS WITH POWER TRANSFORMERS

Just about every electrical device made has some protective system associated with it, even if this is no more than a fuse to protect against current overload, and the protective system has to meet some obvious, and some not so obvious, specifications. For example, a fuse to protect a 13 A mains circuit must be capable of passing 13 A continuously and yet it must not be so rugged that it requires, say, 30 A to blow it. Then there is the time rating to consider. If a current surge of 60 A occurs in a 13 A circuit then the fuse must operate very quickly indeed and certainly before any damage is done to the system being protected. In a high-voltage power system fuses cannot be used to protect against current overloads and protection is provided by very large switches which are triggered by signals derived from measuring devices which monitor the current flow. The problem with a simple fuse is basically one of energy dissipation. At the instant a fuse blows, an arc is produced and if there is sufficient energy available to maintain ionisation of the gas in the arc path then the arc will continue indefinitely. All switchgear on power systems incorporates some kind of cooling process designed to remove energy from the arc path and a process for removing the products of ionisation and replacing them with fresh, sound insulation.

In setting up an overcurrent protection scheme for a power transformer we are attempting to minimise the effects of a short circuit within the transformer. Should such a fault occur we would want to switch the transformer out of circuit before too much damage was done to the transformer and to other parts of the system. An easy way of detecting such a fault would be to compare currents flowing into and out of the transformer. If all is well, these currents should be more or less equal—allowing for the effects of magnetising current. Any out-of-balance can be interpreted as a fault condition.

At this point we come up against a problem, because if such a simple scheme were used then we could find the protective system operating more often than not every time we switched the supply onto the transformer. The effect that causes this maloperation is called magnetic inrush.

We know that if the voltage and flux waveforms in a transformer are assumed to be sinusoidal then the voltage phasor leads the flux phasor by $\pi/2$ radians as shown in figure 36.1a. Let us examine conditions at $\omega t = \pi/2$. The voltage is zero, going negative. The flux it produces must have an instantaneous rate of change equal to zero and growing in magnitude, but negative. Note that it is the change of flux with time that matters; the absolute magnitude of the flux is irrelevant. The flux variation shown in figure 36.1b would satisfy the equation $V = N\,d\Phi/dt$ as effectively as the flux of figure 36.1a.

Imagine then that we were to switch the transformer

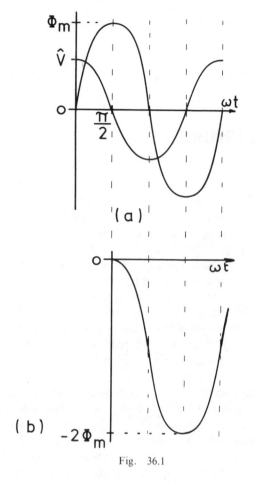

(a)

(b)

Fig. 36.1

on at the instant that the supply voltage was zero going negative. The flux must immediately try to follow the pattern defined in figure 36.1, but if there is no residual magnetism in the transformer then the flux must start at zero and only the flux change of figure 36.1b is possible. The transformer core now has to accommodate a maximum flux of $2\Phi_m$, but if properly designed it will be operating near saturation with the normal maximum flux Φ_m so that it will be forced well into saturation by the flux $2\Phi_m$. The effect on the magnetising current is shown in figure 36.2.

The average value of the peak of the magnetising inrush current can exceed 15% of the average value of the peak of the normal full load current. This has to be compared with the equivalent normal peak magnetising current of about 2% of the full load value. The difficulty that the protection engineer has to face is that the inrush current occurs only in the primary winding, so that an out-of-balance as high as 15% of full load current may be seen by the protection circuit as it compares primary and secondary currents. Obviously, the protective system must not be made to be insensitive to this magnitude of unbalance otherwise it would allow fault currents as high as 15% of full load current to go undetected. And yet, if nothing is done, then the protection will regularly operate when the transformer is switched in. Could we disconnect the protection while the transformer is being energised? This is certainly possible, and since the inrush effect is a transient lasting for about 10 cycles,

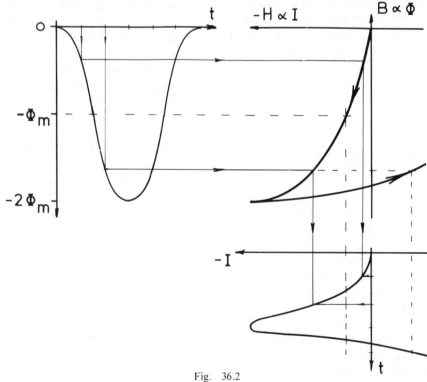

Fig. 36.2

as shown in figure 36.3, we would expect the protection to operate correctly after this interval. But, we must examine the dangers that such an action would bring. A fault occurring in the first few cycles of unprotected operation would be disastrous, so we have to look for an alternative solution.

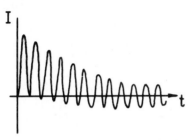

Fig. 36.3

A common solution is to make use of the special features of the inrush current. There is clearly a high harmonic content in this and it transpires that the second harmonic has an amplitude of about 60% of the fundamental. This can be filtered out to be used as a restraining signal to hold back the relay which operates the switchgear.

Overvoltage transients present a different problem. These can occur as a result of lightning discharges to a transmission system or as a result of switching transients. They are characteristically unidirectional impulses with a rise time between 1 and 20 μs. With these fast-rising pulses, the voltage distribution in the winding of the transformer is determined largely by the winding capacitances. To a first approximation, the transformer impedance appears to have the form shown in figure 36.4

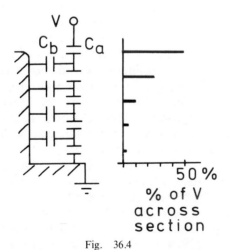

Fig. 36.4

where C_a represents the capacitance between turns and C_b the capacitance between the turns and earth. The graph shows the poor performance of a simple helical

winding under impulse conditions. The problem is largely one of capacitance distribution and high voltage transformers are designed to give a nearly uniform voltage gradient down the windings under impulse conditions. One way of achieving this is to use a disc winding. The conductor is wound into a flat disc and a number of such discs are then stacked around the transformer yoke and connected in series. The arrangement is illustrated in figure 36.5.

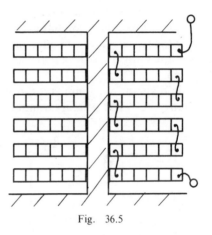

Fig. 36.5

An alternative for very high voltage transformers, over say 300 kV, is the taper layer winding. In this case the total winding is built up of a number of layers wound one upon the other, but the axial length of the layers is reduced as the diameter of the layer increases. This is illustrated in figure 36.6, which also shows how stress shields may be placed at the l.v. and h.v. ends of the winding. Not only does this arrangement give a better surge distribution it also leaves space at the h.v. end for the extra insulation which is needed there.

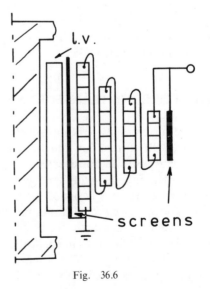

Fig. 36.6

36.3 THE SUMMATION TRANSFORMER

Power system protection engineering provides us with an example of an unusual application of the transformer principle in the summation transformer. The basic requirement is still to compare input and output currents in a circuit, but when the circuit is three-phase with input and output ends separated by distances of 30 km or more the interconnection of the comparators becomes a problem. The difficulty is largely that of providing multiple signal conductors at reasonable cost. The summation transformer minimises this difficulty by combining the signals from the three-phase currents into one resultant. Only one pair of signal, or pilot, wires is then required.

A schematic diagram of a summation transformer is shown in figure 36.7. The primary winding has three

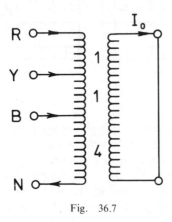

Fig. 36.7

input tappings which are so arranged that currents of 1 A between RN, YN and BN would produce output currents of 6 A, 5 A and 4 A respectively. A balanced three-phase supply would give signal currents of $I/\underline{0^\circ}$ from the red phase, $I/\underline{-120^\circ}$ from the yellow phase and $I/\underline{-240^\circ}$ from the blue phase. The output current would then be the phasor sum of 6 $I/\underline{0^\circ}$, 5 $I/\underline{-120^\circ}$ and 4 $I/\underline{-240^\circ}$ as shown in figure 36.8.

36.4 THE CURRENT TRANSFORMER

When large currents have to be measured it is common practice to step the current down to an acceptable level for metering purposes. A transformer provides a convenient way of doing this with time-varying currents and when a transformer is designed for this particular function it is known as a current transformer. In principle, a current transformer is exactly the same as a voltage transformer, but the differences in application do lead to significantly different features. The primary winding of a current transformer is often only one turn and it is

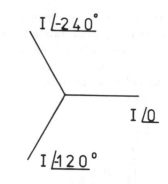

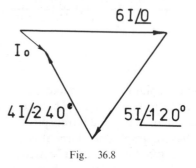

Fig. 36.8

connected in series with the current being measured. The impedance that the transformer presents to the circuit must therefore be very small. Input voltage ceases to have much meaning because the voltage across the primary turn is determined by the current in the winding and the winding impedance; the device is current driven.

The secondary current is a scaled down version of the primary current and its magnitude is fixed by the turns ratio and the magnitude of the primary current. If we were to place a variable resistance R in the secondary circuit then changing its value would not significantly change the secondary current. What would change would be the secondary terminal voltage, defined by I_2R. As this increased in magnitude, the flux in the core would increase until saturation was reached. This would cause distortion of the waveforms and errors in the measurement. In the extreme case, as R tended to infinity, the secondary voltage would become very large, which is why current transformers should never be open-circuited on the secondary.

The secondary load is referred to as the burden and it is an important parameter in measurement circuits which employ current transformers.

The primary current has to supply the magnetising m.m.f. and the transformer losses, so that it is not correct to write $N_1I_1 = N_2I_2$. The error involved may not be very significant in a power transformer, but in a transformer used for measurement such errors have to be carefully evaluated and minimised. The error is not simply one of magnitude. There is an inevitable phase shift between primary and secondary currents which can be very important when the circuit is being used to detect phase shifts or when it is part of a power measuring instrument.

CHAPTER 37

Task 19: Hysteresis and eddy-current loss

T19.1 INTRODUCTION

Hysteresis was mentioned very briefly in Task 17 and we were able to see that there was a power loss associated with the cycle of magnetisation and demagnetisation in ferromagnetic materials. Time-varying fluxes will also give rise to induced e.m.f.s and if these e.m.f.s exist in closed conducting loops then currents will circulate. These loops need not consist of specially arranged conductors; any conducting path in the supporting structure of an electrical device, or even in adjacent steelwork, will have an e.m.f. induced in it if it is linked with a time-varying magnetic flux. The circulating currents will cause a power loss which is additional to the hysteresis loss of the magnetisation cycle.

T19.2 OBJECTIVES

When you have finished this Task you should be able to do the following:

(a) write a short report explaining qualitatively why hysteresis and eddy-current losses occur in electrical equipment;
(b) determine the hysteresis loss per cycle in a volume of iron for which the B-H loop is known;
(c) quote the experimentally derived relationship between hysteresis loss per unit volume, maximum flux density and frequency;
(d) quote the relationship between eddy-current loss, maximum flux density and frequency; and
(e) given the necessary experimental data, determine the eddy-current and hysteresis loss components of the total core loss within an electric machine.

T19.3 PRIOR WORK

It will be assumed that you have satisfactorily completed Tasks 15 and 17.

T19.4 HYSTERESIS LOSS

When considering the magnetic effects of ferromagnetic materials we explained the hysteresis effect in terms of the domain theory of magnetism. According to this theory, when we place a ferromagnetic material in an externally generated magnetic field, magnetically polarised regions within the material align themselves with the external field. Reversal of the field causes a reversal of the domain alignment. These changes are physically detectable and can give rise to observable changes in the dimensions of a magnetic material. Common experience should tell us that we cannot change the shape of a material without expending energy. Thus there must be a power loss associated with the continuous cyclic changes of domain alignment in magnetic materials subjected to alternating magnetisation.

We predicted this loss in section T17.6 when we proved that the energy used to establish a magnetic flux density B in a nonlinear material with hysteresis exceeded the energy released by the field as the magnetic field strength was reduced to zero. The difference in energy is the energy lost in re-aligning the domains.

The energy lost as we run the material around one complete cycle of the hysteresis loop is given by

$$U = \int_{B_1}^{B_1} H \, \mathrm{d}B$$

and the units are joules per unit volume.

At a frequency f, the rate of energy loss, or power loss, is

$$P_h = Uf$$

joules per unit volume per second, or watts per unit volume.

If we know the maximum flux density that is reached in the cycle and if we have the B-H loop for the material corresponding to this maximum value then we can determine the power loss per unit volume as the area bounded by the loop times the frequency.

There is an experimentally derived relationship

between power loss, frequency and maximum flux density which holds true over the normal working range of flux density. This is:

$$P_h = \lambda_h f B_m^x$$

The constant λ_h is known as the Steinmetz coefficient and its value varies from material to material. The value of the constant x also depends on the type of material, but the range of variation is small about a typical value of 1.6.

T19.5 EDDY-CURRENT LOSS

We can only make an approximate analysis here for the eddy-current loss in a block of conducting material. Such a block is shown in figure T19.1. It is assumed that a sinusoidally-varying flux density B crosses the face of the block at right angles and flows parallel to the long side d. The flux density is assumed to be uniform across the face.

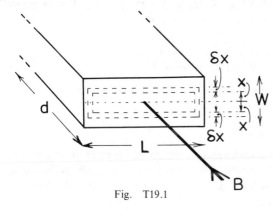

Fig. T19.1

We now imagine a thin conducting loop formed by two thin strips of width δx, length L and separated by a distance $2x$ as shown in the diagram. The ends of the loop are closed by short conducting paths of length $2x$. Through this loop there will be a flux $\delta\Phi$ given approximately by:

$$\delta\Phi = B_m \sin \omega t \, 2xL$$

As this flux varies with time there will be an e.m.f. induced in the loop of magnitude v, where

$$v = \frac{d\Phi}{dt} = B_m \omega \cos \omega t \, 2xL$$

This will cause a current to circulate around the loop and the current will be limited by the resistance R of the loop, where

$$R = \frac{\rho 2L}{d\,\delta x}$$

The power loss in the loop is v^2/R, and the total in-

stantaneous power loss in the block, p_e, is the sum of v^2/R for all possible loops as x varies from 0 to $W/2$.

$$\therefore p_e = \int_0^{W/2} \frac{B_m^2 \omega^2 \cos^2 \omega t \, 2L\,d}{\rho} x^2 \, dx$$

The mean value is given by

$$P_e = \frac{B_m^2 \omega^2 L\,d}{3\rho} \left(\frac{W}{2}\right)^3$$

The important conclusions that we can draw from this are that:

(i) $P_e \propto B_m^2$;
(ii) $P_e \propto f^2$;
(iii) $P_e \propto 1/\rho$; and
(iv) if we have a block of identical width W made up of N laminations each of width W/N, then, provided that the laminations are insulated from each other, the value of P_e is reduced by a factor of $1/N^2$.

We can now see why the magnetic cores of transformers and machines are built up from thin sheets of steel. You will also find that large current-carrying conductors are often made up of several small-section conductors connected electrically in parallel but insulated from each other in the manner shown in figure T19.2. This arrangement again reduces eddy-current loss which would result from any time-varying fluxes which might thread the conductors. It also gives better mechanical flexibility.

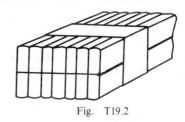

Fig. T19.2

T19.6 TOTAL CORE LOSS

Within an electrical machine hysteresis and eddy-current losses will occur simultaneously. The total core loss will be the sum of these two components and can be written as:

$$P_c = P_h + P_e$$

$$P_c = K_h f B_m^x + K_e f^2 B_m^2 \qquad \text{(T19.1)}$$

where K_h and K_e are constants which may be determined experimentally.

As an example of this let us suppose that we have measured the power loss in a d.c. machine at different speeds but with the same field excitation. We obtain values for the core loss by subtracting the I^2R loss from the total power loss. In a particular test this gives a core loss of 2200 W at 1000 r.p.m. and 800 W at 500 r.p.m. Because the flux density is constant and assuming that the frequency of the induced e.m.f. in the rotor is proportional to the rotational speed, we can write equation T19.1 as:

$$P_c = K_1 N + K_1 N^2$$

Thus:

$$2200 = K_1 \ 10^3 + K_2 \ 10^6,$$

and

$$800 = K_1 \ 0.5 \ 10^3 + K_2 \ 0.25 \ 10^6$$

from which

$$K_1 = 1.0 \quad \text{and} \quad K_2 = 1.2 \ 10^{-3}$$

With this information we can now predict the core loss in the machine at different load conditions. For example, let us assume that the core material is a common material for which the constant x in equation T19.1 is 1.6. What are the components of core loss when the machine runs at 1500 r.p.m. with the excitation increased by 20%?

At 1000 r.p.m., $P_c = 1.0 \ 10^3 + 1.2 \ 10^{-3} \ 10^6$ W
At 1500 r.p.m., $P_c = 1.0 \ 1.5 \ 10^3 + 1.2 \ 10^{-3} \ 2.25 \ 10^6$ W
At 1500 r.p.m., with B_m increased by a factor of 1.2,
$P_c = (1.2)^{1.6} \ 1.5 \ 10^3 + (1.2)^2 \ 1.2 \ 10^{-3} \ 2.25 \ 10^6$ W

$$P_c = 2.0 + 3.9 \ \text{kW}$$

T19.7   SELF-ASSESSMENT QUESTIONS

Question 1

The hysteresis loops given in figure T19.3 are for the same sample of steel at maximum flux densities of 0.8 T and 1.0 T. Determine the energy loss per cycle per cubic metre in this material at the maximum flux densities given.

If the hysteresis loss is proportional to B_m^x, determine the value of x for this material.

Question 2

Determine the energy loss per cycle per cubic metre and the power loss per cubic metre at 50 Hz for the material which has the magnetic characteristic shown in figure T19.4.

Question 3

When a transformer is connected to a supply of frequency 50 Hz the core loss is composed of 200 W due to hysteresis and 50 W due to eddy-currents. Determine the total core loss when the transformer is connected to a 60 Hz supply if the flux density in the core is unaltered.

Question 4

When a transformer is connected to a 200 V, 50 Hz supply the loss in the core is made up of 400 W due to hysteresis and 100 W due to eddy-currents. If the supply voltage is increased to 250 V at 50 Hz determine the total core loss. Assume that hysteresis loss is proportional to B_m^2.

Question 5

The power loss due to hysteresis in a transformer core is 750 W at 50 Hz and with $B_m = 1.5$ T. Determine the power loss in the core when

(a) $B_m = 1.5$ T, $f = 60$ Hz, and
(b) $B_m = 1.25$ T, $f = 60$ Hz.

Take $P_h \propto B_m^2$

Question 6

A transformer is designed to operate from a 10 kV 60 Hz supply. The power loss in the core is then made up of 1800 W due to hysteresis and 700 W due to eddy currents.

Determine the total power loss in the core when the transformer is operated from a 6.6 kV 50 Hz supply. Take $P_h \propto B_m^{1.6}$.

T19.8   ANSWERS AND SOLUTIONS

1. (a) $U_h = 1.6 \times 400 = 640$ J m^{-3}
   (b) $U_h = 2.0 \times 500 = 1000$ J m^{-3}
   (c) $U_h = KB^x \ 1000 = K(1)^x, \therefore K = 1000$
       $640 = 1000(0.8)^x$, hence $x = 2$.

2. Energy loss per cycle per cubic metre $= 1920$ J
   Power loss per cubic metre $= 96$ kW

3. $P_c = K_1 f + K_2 f^2$ when B_m is constant
   at 50 Hz, $P_c = 200 + 50$ W
   at 60 Hz, $P_c = 200\frac{6}{5} + 50\frac{6}{5} = 312$ W

4. $P_c = K_a B_m^2 + K_B B_m^2 = K_c B_m^2$ when f is constant
   at 200 V, 50 Hz, $V_1 = 200 = K_D B_{m1}$
   at 250 V, 50 Hz, $V_1 = 250 = K_D B_{m2}$

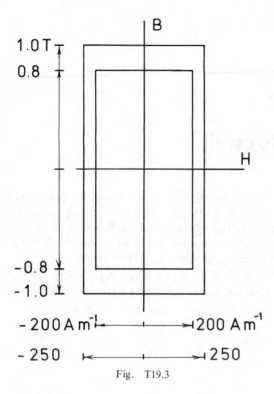

Fig. T19.3

$\therefore B_{m2} = 1.25\, B_{m1}$ and
P_c at 250 V $= 500\,(1.25)^2 = 780$ W.

5. When $B = 1.5$ T, $f = 50$ Hz, $P_h = 750$ W
When $B = 1.5$ T, $f = 60$ Hz, $P_c = 750\frac{6}{5} = 900$ W
When $B = 1.25$ T, $f = 60$ Hz, $P_c = 900(1.25/1.5)^2 = 625$ W

6. $P_c = K_h f B_m^{1.6} + K_c f^2 B_m^2$

$= 1800 + 700$ W, initially.

The change in condition demands a change in B_m since in case 1 $V_1 = 10^4 = 4.44\, f_1 B_1 A N_1$ and
in case 2 $V_1 = 6.6\ 10^3 = 4.44\, f_2 B_2 A N_1$
$\therefore B_2 = 0.79\, B_1$.
Under new conditions therefore,
$P_c = 1800(\tfrac{5}{6})(0.79)^{1.6} + 700(\tfrac{5}{6})^2(0.79)^2 = 1333$ W

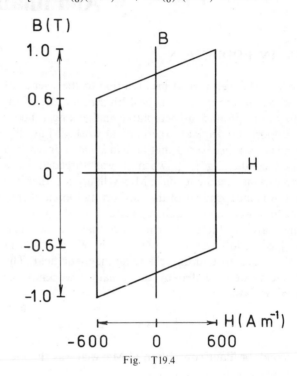

Fig. T19.4

CHAPTER 38

And finally, Maxwell

38.1 INTRODUCTION

When Maxwell turned his attention to the science of electricity in the middle of the 19th century one of his aims was to produce an acceptable mathematical theory to support the original experimental work of Faraday. Faraday had discovered that an e.m.f. was induced in a closed conducting loop when it was threaded by a time-varying magnetic flux. Maxwell argued that the e.m.f. was independent of the conducting loop and that if the loop were removed then an electric field would still remain around the contour in space that the loop had occupied. It followed that there was an electric field in all the space around any changing magnetic field. The two fields were related by the equation we know as Faraday's law,

$$e = \oint E \, \mathrm{d}s = -\frac{\mathrm{d}\Phi}{\mathrm{d}t}$$

A second, brilliant conception of Maxwell was the idea of displacement current. We met this in Chapter 24 and saw how we could use it to extend Ampère's law to give

$$\oint H \, \mathrm{d}s = I + \frac{\mathrm{d}\Psi}{\mathrm{d}t}$$

But, without doubt, Maxwell's most astonishing contribution was his prediction of electromagnetic waves in free space.

The importance of electromagnetic field theory cannot be underestimated. There are very obvious applications of the theory in radio communications, but it is just as applicable in the design of electrical machines and in the analysis of the performance of long transmission lines. In this final chapter we shall avoid a very detailed mathematical analysis and attempt to show simply how a particular system of current carrying conductors gives rise to electromagnetic waves in space.

38.2 MATHEMATICAL TERMINOLOGY

We shall be using a notation for differentiation that may be new to you. In certain cases, instead of writing $\mathrm{d}/\mathrm{d}x$ we shall write $\partial/\partial x$. This sign tells us that the term we are differentiating may be a function of more than one variable, but that we must consider all variables except x constant when we differentiate.

Thus if $P = K_0 + K_1 x + K_2 y + K_3 z$, where x, y and z are variables and K represents a constant, then

$$\frac{\partial P}{\partial x} = K_1$$

$$\frac{\partial P}{\partial y} = K_2$$

$$\frac{\partial P}{\partial z} = K_3$$

38.3 SIGN CONVENTIONS

The sign convention which defines the positive sense of the flux Φ produced by a current I has been described as the right-hand-screw rule. The convention is important in the application of the circuital law where, you will remember, we sum the product $H\delta s$ along a closed path around a current I. The direction that we follow around the path is the assumed direction of the positive flux produced by the current I.

Fig. 38.1

The convention for the positive sense of an induced e.m.f. in a closed loop which is threaded by a changing flux also follows a right-handed rotation, but in this case confusion often arises because the assumed positive sense of the e.m.f. is at odds with what one would expect.

Let us first examine what really happens in a case such as the one illustrated in figure 38.2. The current I_1

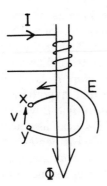

Fig. 38.2

establishes a flux Φ with positive senses shown and we assume that I_1 and Φ are increasing positive. The time changing flux establishes an electric field in the space about it and a conducting loop placed in the field is influenced by it. The positive charge in the loop is driven around the loop in such a sense that if the loop is broken at X and Y the terminal X becomes positive with respect to Y. If X and Y are joined then a current I_2 flows from X through the connection to Y and then around the loop. The sense of I_2 is opposite to the sense of I_1.

We can write: $V_{XY} = \mathrm{d}\Phi/\mathrm{d}t = \int E\,\mathrm{d}s =$ the e.m.f. in the loop, where E is defined as the electric field produced by the time-varying flux and is taken to be acting in the sense shown in figure 38.2. The path of integration for $E\,\mathrm{d}s$ follows the line of action of E. This relationship satisfies Faraday's law which states that an e.m.f. is produced which is proportional to $\mathrm{d}\Phi/\mathrm{d}t$. It also satisfies Lenz's law which tells us that the direction of the induced e.m.f. is in a sense which will cause a current flow which will produce a magnetic field to oppose the original change in Φ.

In more complex situations we cannot rely on getting the signs and directions right by inspection and we must stay with an accepted convention. The convention follows a right-hand rule and is defined in figure 38.3.

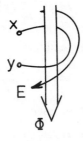

Fig. 38.3

We say that the e.m.f. is produced by an electric field E which has the usual right-hand-screw relationship with Φ. The e.m.f., which we shall now call e, is again given by

$e = \int E\,\mathrm{d}s$ but this time we sum in the sense of E in figure 38.3. The magnitude of e is given by Faraday's law, $e = \mathrm{d}\Phi/\mathrm{d}t$, as before. The correct sense of e is allowed for by writing:

$$e = -\frac{\mathrm{d}\Phi}{\mathrm{d}t} = \int E\,\mathrm{d}s \qquad (38.1)$$

38.4 WAVE PROPAGATION IN FREE SPACE

I should like to refer you back to question 4 in Task 11 in which we examined the magnetic field distribution about two flat plates carrying a steady current I. We established that the magnetic flux density above and below the plates was constant, within the limits of our approximations. Now let us see what happens if we allow the plate current to vary with time. We shall use two basic equations:

$$\oint H\,\mathrm{d}s = \frac{\mathrm{d}\Psi}{\mathrm{d}t},$$

and

$$\oint E\,\mathrm{d}s = -\frac{\mathrm{d}\Phi}{\mathrm{d}t}$$

You should recognise these as Ampère's law and Faraday's law, respectively, and in each case the integration is carried out around a closed path.

Figure 38.4 reproduces part of the system of question 4 with the addition of co-ordinate axes representing positive directions of x, y and z. For d.c. conditions the

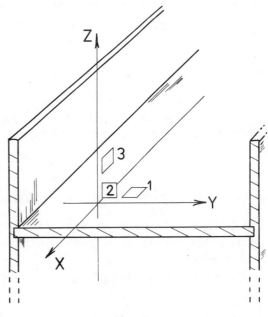

Fig. 38.4

flux density vector B is parallel to y at all points and constant everywhere. Now let B vary with time.

To examine the situation fully we use three exploratory loops, one in each of the ree co-ordinate planes. The only loop which is threaded by a time-varying magnetic flux is loop 3. Around this loop therefore, we have

$$\oint E \, ds = -\frac{\partial \Phi}{\partial t}$$

and $\int E \, ds$ must be finite. There can be no changing E field in the z direction, otherwise we would have a change in electric flux through loop 1 which would imply a value of $\int H \, ds$ around it. If B is constant at a fixed distance above the current plate and has no component along x then $\int H \, ds$ about 1 must be zero. Therefore E_z is zero.

Conditions about loop 3 are illustrated in figure 38.5.

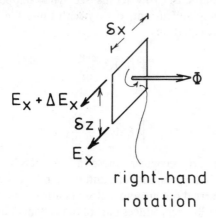

Fig. 38.5

E_x is assumed acting in the $+x$ direction and E_x must vary with z. If we denote the variation as $\partial E_x/\partial z$ then the difference in E_x values along the two sides parallel to x is given by

$$\Delta E_x = \frac{\partial E_x}{\partial z} \delta z$$

Thus

$$-E_x \delta x + \left(E_x + \frac{\partial E_x}{\partial z} \delta z\right) \delta x = -\frac{\partial \Phi}{\partial t} = -\delta_z \delta_x \mu_0 \frac{\partial H_y}{\partial t}$$

or

$$\frac{\partial E_x}{\partial z} = -\mu_0 \frac{\partial H_y}{\partial t} \tag{38.2}$$

Now, if E acts in the sense of $+x$ and is time-varying then there will be a change of electric flux across loop 2 and we can write:

$$\oint H \, ds = \frac{\partial \Psi}{\partial t} \tag{38.3}$$

The vector H has no component in the z direction, so

conditions in loop 3 are as defined in figure 38.6. Note that we have had to allow for a change in the magnitude of H_y as z increases. This is the only way that we can satisfy equation 38.3. It conflicts with our initial hypothesis that B, and therefore H, is the same at all points, so let us re-examine that hypothesis. We were claiming that at any instant in time B was everywhere the same. This is acceptable if we can also accept that a change in the current is felt instantaneously at all points in space so that, as the current changes, the flux densities at the surface and at a large distance from the surface both change at precisely the same instant. This is most unlikely and our initial hypothesis appears to be suspect.

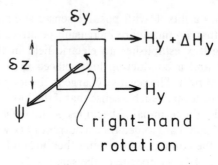

Fig. 38.6

Let us continue therefore with the situation described in figure 38.6 in which H_y is assumed to vary with z. The change in H_y over a small distance δz is therefore:

$$\Delta H_y = \frac{\partial H_y}{\partial z} \delta z$$

so that

$$H_y \delta y - \left(H_y + \frac{\partial H_y}{\partial z} \delta z\right) \delta y = \frac{\partial \Psi}{\partial t} = \delta y \delta z \varepsilon_0 \frac{\partial E_x}{\partial t}$$

$$\frac{\partial H_y}{\partial z} = -\varepsilon_0 \frac{\partial E_x}{\partial t} \tag{38.4}$$

From equation 38.2 we obtain

$$\frac{\partial^2 E_x}{\partial z \partial t} = -\mu_0 \frac{\partial^2 H_y}{\partial t^2}$$

From equation 38.4 we obtain

$$\frac{\partial^2 E_x}{\partial t \partial z} = -\frac{1}{\varepsilon_0} \frac{\partial^2 H_y}{\partial z^2}$$

and these two equations give

$$\frac{\partial^2 H_y}{\partial z^2} = \mu_0 \varepsilon_0 \frac{\partial^2 H_y}{\partial t^2} \tag{38.5}$$

By a similar process we can show that

$$\frac{\partial^2 E_x}{\partial z^2} = \mu_0 \varepsilon_0 \frac{\partial^2 E_x}{\partial t^2} \tag{38.6}$$

These two equations are the wave propagation equations for the H field and the E field. If we restrict ourselves to considering sinusoidally varying quantities we can adopt standard solutions for these equations as follows:

$$H_y = H_m \sin \frac{2\pi}{\lambda}(z \pm ct)$$

$$E_x = E_m \sin \frac{2\pi}{\lambda}(z \pm ct)$$

where λ is the wavelength, $c = (\varepsilon_0 \mu_0)^{-1/2}$, and the frequency is $f = c/\lambda$. Note that c must have the dimensions of velocity. It is in fact equal to the velocity of light.

Let us take first the solution with the negative sign. At $t = 0$.

$$H_y = H_m \sin \frac{2\pi z}{\lambda}$$

and

$$E_x = E_m \sin \frac{2\pi z}{\lambda}$$

These equations are interpreted in figure 38.7. In particular we see that H_y and E_x are zero at $t = 0$, $z = 0$. Now let a time $t = 1/c$ pass. H_y and E_x are now zero for $(z - ct) = 0$, or $z = 1$. The whole pattern of H and E has moved up the z axis; in fact the waves are travelling along the z axis with the velocity of light.

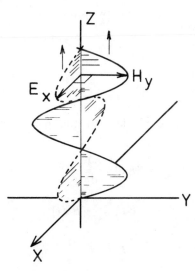

Fig. 38.7

If we take the second solution with $(z + ct)$ we can show that this represents waves travelling in the minus-z direction with the velocity of light. A real situation may involve both types of waves.

We have shown then that the simple conductor arrangement of figure 38.4 will produce electromagnetic waves which propagate into space along the z axis with the velocity of light when a time-varying current flows in the conductor.

38.5 MAXWELL'S EQUATION

The four basic equations of electromagnetism are known collectively as Maxwell's equations. They are stated as follows:

$$\oint H \, ds = I + \frac{d\Psi}{dt}$$

$$\oint E \, ds = -\frac{d\Phi}{dt}$$

$$\int\int \varepsilon_0 E_n \, dS = Q$$

$$\int\int B_n \, dS = 0$$

This last equation has not been formally stated in this form elsewhere in this book. It says that if we integrate the magnetic flux density over a closed surface it sums to zero: i.e. flux in equals flux out. It is the flux continuity law that we first met in our work on magnetic circuits.

There are three other equations that are needed to support the above four. They bring in the material properties and are:

for dielectric materials, $D = \varepsilon E$
for magnetic materials, $B = \mu H$, and
for conducting materials, $E = J\rho$

38.6 AN EXAMPLE

Figure 38.8 shows a large, air-spaced, parallel-plate capacitor which is used as a strip line. It is charged by closing the switch S at $t = 0$. After time t, charge has travelled with velocity u a distance L along the plates and conditions for $x < L$ are as given on the figure.

Assuming that q is the charge density in $C \, m^{-2}$,

(a) write down E in terms of q and ε_0;
(b) obtain an expression for I in terms of q, u and the plate dimensions;
(c) obtain an expression for H in terms of I and the plate dimensions;
(d) hence show that the magnetic flux density across the space between the plates is given by

$$B = \mu_0 \varepsilon_0 E u; \quad \text{and}$$

(e) by applying Faraday's law to the region around the charging zone obtain an alternative expression for B and hence show that,

$$u = \frac{1}{\sqrt{\mu_0 \varepsilon_0}}$$

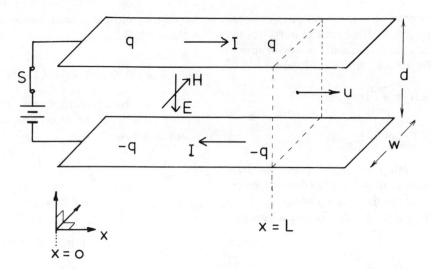

Fig. 38.8

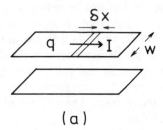

(a)

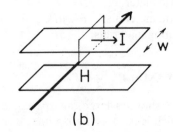

(b)

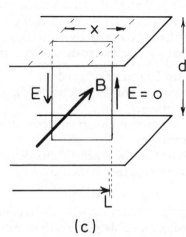

(c)

Fig. 38.9

Solution

(a) $q = D = \varepsilon_0 E$

(b) The element of charge on the length x in figure 38.9a is $\delta q = qw\delta x$.

The current I is $\delta q / \delta t$ which becomes, in the limit,

$$I = qw \frac{dx}{dt} = qwu$$

(c) Applying the circuital law about the path shown in figure 38.9b,

$$Hw = I$$

(d) $\quad Hw = qwu$

$\therefore H = qu$

$\therefore B = \mu_0 qu = \mu_0 \varepsilon_0 E u$

(e) Applying Faraday's law to the path shown in figure 38.9c,

$$-\int E \, dl = \frac{d\Phi}{dt}$$

$$-[-E \, d] = \frac{d}{dt}[B \, dx]$$

$$E \, d = B d \frac{dx}{dt}$$

$$\therefore E = Bu$$

comparing this to the solution for part (d) we can see that

$$u = \frac{1}{\sqrt{\mu_0 \, \varepsilon_0}}$$

Index